Young Reader's Edition

THE SEA

Leonard Engel

and the Editors of TIME-LIFE BOOKS

TIME-LIFE BOOKS, NEW YORK

ON THE COVER: A giant wave, whipped up by a storm hundreds of miles away, crashes into Waimea Bay in the Hawaiian Islands.

TIME
LIFE
BOOKS
®

LIFE WORLD LIBRARY

LIFE NATURE LIBRARY

TIME READING PROGRAM

THE LIFE HISTORY OF THE UNITED STATES

LIFE SCIENCE LIBRARY

GREAT AGES OF MAN

TIME-LIFE LIBRARY OF ART

TIME-LIFE LIBRARY OF AMERICA

FOODS OF THE WORLD

THIS FABULOUS CENTURY

LIFE LIBRARY OF PHOTOGRAPHY

Contents

Introduction

Despite the importance of the sea to mankind, oceanography, the scientific study of the great waters of the earth, has been quite neglected until recently. Since World War II, though, more and more scientists have been turning their attention to the sea. Marine laboratories are expanding rapidly and many students are being trained in all aspects of oceanography. This new interest is not confined to the United States; all maritime nations are taking part. Throughout the world, hundreds of technically trained people, on scores of research ships, are at present working at sea; and many thousands more are studying the results of that work in laboratories ashore. What can we expect from this large increase in scientific effort? Clearly it will help plug a big gap in our knowledge of the earth. But it will do much more. As we learn more about the sea, we can improve our natural defenses and marine transportation, exert some control on the climate, and make available a vast new source of food, a source now barely tapped. In its natural state the sea today produces, acre for acre, about as much as the land, and yet man takes only about 2 per cent of his food from the water. This book covers all of these aspects of oceanography and also looks toward the future, when man will have to make greater use of the sea if his increasing population is to survive. Here is an excellent introduction to a fascinating subject.

COLUMBUS O'DONNELL ISELIN
Senior Physical Oceanographer
Woods Hole Oceanographic Institution

1

The Mysteries of the Watery Depths

Our planet has the wrong name. Our ancestors, who believed that the sea was only a narrow river surrounding the rocks and soil on which they lived, named this planet Earth, after the land they found all around them. If they had known what the earth was really like, they undoubtedly would have named it Ocean, after the tremendous areas of water that cover almost three fourths of its surface.

In the sun's family of planets the earth is unique in its possession of oceans. Indeed it is remarkable that oceans exist at all. They do only because the largest part of the earth has a surface temperature in the small range within which water remains a liquid: in short, between 32° F. (below which, under ordinary conditions, water freezes) and 212° F. (when it boils and becomes a gas).

In a surprising variety of ways, the prop-

GILDED BY LIGHT, a stretch of ocean reaches to the horizon and beyond. Though apparently deserted, these vast waters brim with countless living forms. Here dwell plants and animals so small they cannot be seen by the naked eye. Here also is the home of the blue whale, a giant that averages 100 feet in length.

7

erties of liquid water seem almost to have been purposely designed to make the world a place where life can exist. Water has an unusually high capacity for storing heat, for example. As a result, the oceans act as great heat reservoirs that cool the earth in summer and warm it in winter.

Another important characteristic of water is that it can dissolve more substances than any other liquid known. No life could exist on earth for a moment if water did not have this capability. Living organisms, big and small, are chemical factories that carry on the business of life by means of an amazing variety of chemical reactions. Many of these reactions can take place only when water is present to dissolve the reacting substances and bring their molecules together. Furthermore, water forms part of many of the chemical compounds found in living tissue. Seventy per cent of the human body is water. All forms of life need water—which, even for plants and animals that live on land, must come ultimately from the oceans.

The oceans' unique importance to life is equaled by their great size. Together they

A Stubborn Survivor

Sea lilies, animals with flowerlike bodies, have been discovered in fossil form in rock that is more than 300 million years old (*left*). Unlike other ancient marine creatures that are now extinct, sea lilies adapted to life in the sea so well that they still survive in a form (*right*) very little changed from their early ancestors.

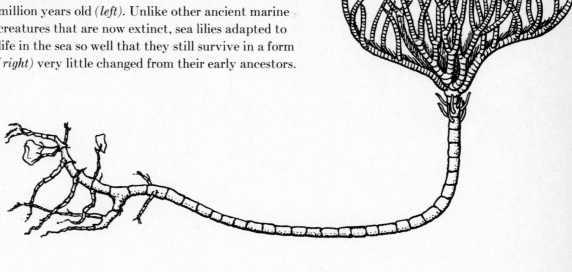

cover 141 million square miles, more than two thirds of the entire surface of the earth. The largest of the four oceans is the Pacific (equal in size to the other three oceans combined): then come the Atlantic, the Indian, and the Arctic. With their fringing gulfs and smaller seas, they make up an interconnected system that forms a girdle around the globe. The oceans contain 330 million cubic miles of water; the volume of all land above sea level is only one eighteenth as great. The tallest peak on land, 29,028-foot-high Mount Everest, could be sunk without a trace in

the greatest sea canyon, the 35,800-foot-deep Mariana Trench in the western Pacific. Locked up in all this water is a great variety of chemicals and minerals in solution. Oxygen, carbon dioxide and nitrogen from the atmosphere are found dissolved in sea water. Dissolved oxygen is what marine creatures breathe. Dissolved carbon dioxide is used by green plants in the sea to produce food. But so far as anyone knows, dissolved nitrogen serves no purpose in the sea.

The most noticeable of the ocean's chemicals is sodium chloride—ordinary table salt,

9

which is what makes sea water taste salty. Sea water is about 3.5 per cent salt; a cubic mile of sea water contains 166 million tons of salt, and the sea as a whole contains enough salt to cover the continents with a layer 500 feet thick.

Where does all the salt in the sea come from? Part of it has come from the breaking up of rocks by frost and erosion. This gradual wearing away of mountains has released salt and other chemicals locked up in the rock and allowed them to be dissolved by rain water and carried down to the ocean. The rest of the salt has been soaked out of rocks beneath the ocean bed.

The chemicals that have washed from the land into the ocean are only a tiny part of the total material that finds its way to the sea. The ocean is the earth's great catch basin. Sooner or later almost everything ends up there. Black mud that once grew corn and cotton in the Mississippi Valley, debris from the grinding down of a hundred mountain ranges, the scourings from ten thousand

river channels—all of these are on the ocean bottom. So are dust, volcanic ash and even tiny meteorite globules from outer space.

To this mixture is added the debris that the sea itself creates. When marine organisms die, their remains drift downward. A part of this unending "rain" never reaches the bottom because it is eaten on the way down by deeper-dwelling organisms or because it is dissolved by sea water. Over a long period of time, however, a great quantity of marine debris settles on the ocean floor.

The shells of extinct sea life are certainly there, and it may be that the mud would reveal the imprints of even more ancient soft-bodied creatures—undisturbed for billions of years, crumbled by no wind, battered by no wave. In the ooze at the bottom of the ocean, the quiet is more profound than anywhere else in the world. By penetrating far into the sediments that lie there, scientists may learn some astonishing things about the dawn of life on this planet.

Through most of his history man has been

Descendant of an Extinct Species

The horseshoe crab (*above*) is a sea animal that has remained almost unchanged over millions of years of evolution. On the other hand, an ancestor of the horseshoe, the giant trilobite (*left*), is now extinct. The fossil trilobite shown here, about 18 inches long, is one of the multitude that ruled the earth as sea-floor scavengers for about 370 million years.

studying only the surface of the sea, as a source of food and as an avenue for travel. Now he is beginning to plumb the ocean depths. Although man's knowledge of these great depressions is still very skimpy, there has been more sounding and exploration of the ocean bottom in the last 20 years than in all the rest of history.

The depth record for manned undersea exploration is held by the crew of the *Trieste*. This vessel, a type called a bathyscaphe, was designed to penetrate the depths of the ocean, and on January 23, 1960, it spent 20 minutes on the bottom, deep inside the Mariana Trench—nearly seven miles down. But most of man's present knowledge of the depths has not come from such record-breaking achievements. We have learned about the ocean bottom in the way we have been learning about space—by inventing instruments and techniques to bring back information from places to which a man cannot easily go.

Already some astonishing discoveries have been made. One of the most unexpected is that there are significant geological differences between the land and ocean areas. Oceanographers, scientists who study the sea, now know that the land and sea are distinctly different. The continents are made of granitic rock; the bed of the deep ocean, however, consists of a heavier kind of rock called basalt. Another piece of surprising new knowledge is that the earth's crust—the thin outermost layer—is far thinner un-

der the sea than it is on land. Equally extraordinary was the recent discovery of a 40,000-mile undersea mountain range, by far the longest in the world and now named the Mid-Ocean Ridge.

But not even this new knowledge of geology is as surprising as the startling variety and interest of life in the sea. No one can make an accurate guess at the number of individual organisms that live there. Scientists have not even completed their lists of the kinds of things that live there. New species are found by almost every expedition that sets out.

The life of the ocean is divided into distinct zones, each with its own group of creatures that feed upon each other and depend on each other in different ways. There is, first of all, the tidal zone, where land and sea meet. Then comes the zone of the shallow seas around the continents, a region that goes down to about 500 feet. It is in these two zones that the vast majority of all marine life occurs. The deep ocean adds two regions, the zone of light and the zone of perpetual darkness. When the *Trieste* descended into the clear waters of the western Pacific, light could still be seen through its portholes at a depth of 1,000 feet. But for practical purposes the zone of light ends at about 600 feet. Below that level there is too little light to support the growth of the "grass" of the sea—the tiny, single-celled green plants whose ability to form sugar and starch with the aid of sunlight makes them the ultimate

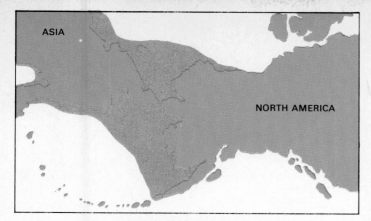

NORTH AMERICA AND ASIA

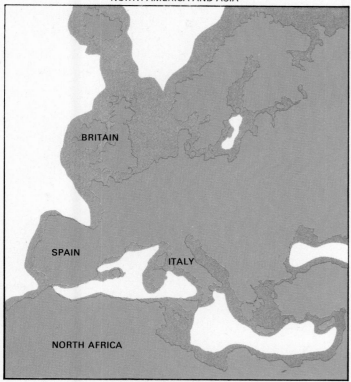

GREATER EUROPE

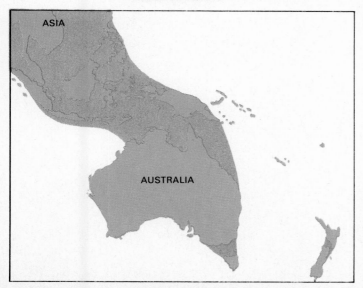

AUSTRALIA AND SOUTHEAST ASIA

Land Bridges of the Past

The earth did not always look as it does today. Hundreds of thousands of years ago, continents now separated by water were joined by land bridges. Thus, animals and plants that first evolved in Asia could pass by land to North America (*left, top*). It is believed that the first humans in North America came by this same land bridge. The European land bridges (*left, middle*) show how Britain was once linked to the continent and Spain and Italy were once joined to North Africa. The Australian land bridge (*left, bottom*), connecting the island continent to Asia, was perhaps the first to vanish beneath the sea.

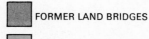

FORMER LAND BRIDGES

THE CONTINENTS TODAY

13

source of all things that live in the ocean.

The natural history of the sea and development, or evolution, of the plants and animals that live there are really the story of life itself. For all animals—including man—and all plants that now live on the land descend from organisms that once lived in the sea.

The sea is old, old almost beyond imagining. And the earth itself is still older. Most scientists believe that the earth was born some four to six billion years ago but that the sea did not begin to fill with water from great overhanging rain clouds until some time later.

Some say life appeared on earth two billion years ago or possibly even earlier. Some put the time a little nearer the present. There is no clear-cut evidence from which the date can be determined. The assumption of modern science is that the first "living" things must have been molecules possessing the ability to reproduce themselves—the property that above all distinguishes living things from nonliving. These molecules must have first taken shape in the sea, because water was necessary to their formation.

These living molecules eventually led to the evolution of simple, single-celled organisms. To live, these first creatures of the sea had to consume smaller molecules of the proper kind. Then a second event undoubtedly happened, almost as important as the leap into life itself. Certain living organisms acquired the ability to capture energy from

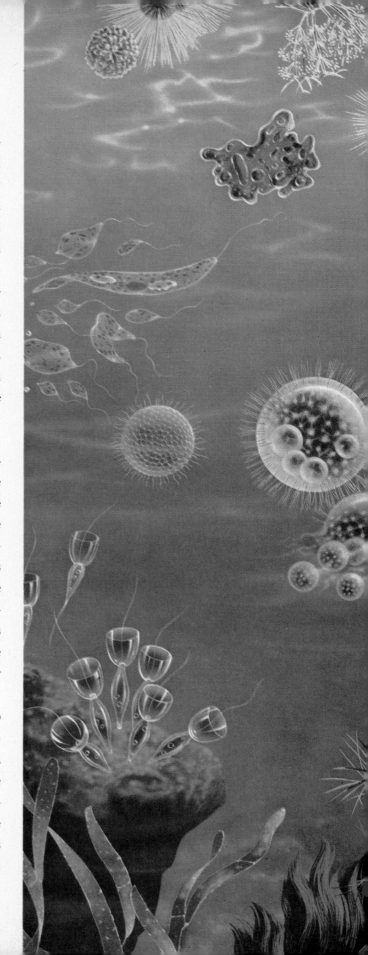

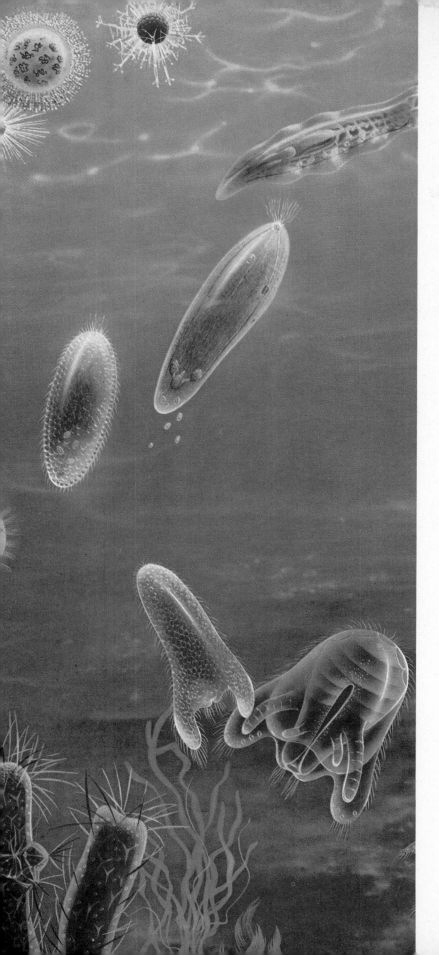

The Basis of All Life

Blobs of protoplasm—simple plants and animals called protistans—float in the sea. These tiny objects are believed to be modern descendants of the first forms in which life appeared. Protistans are eaten by slightly larger creatures, which in turn are consumed by still larger sea dwellers and so on up the ladder. Thus, the protistans are the basic building blocks of life in the sea.

15

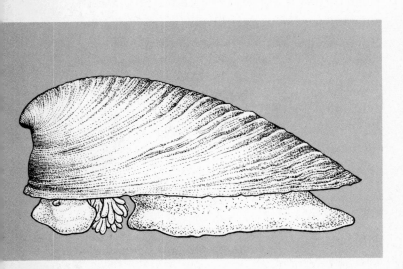

sunlight and use it to make food out of the chemicals dissolved in the sea. These living things took the carbon dioxide that is dissolved in sea water and, by using sunlight, were able to produce sugar, at the same time releasing oxygen.

The ability to perform these complicated acts was not acquired all at once, but over a long period and in several stages. The organisms involved in this process were plants. Other organisms, unable to perform this miracle (called photosynthesis) but still needing organic food, found that they could live on plants. These were animals.

From the day life first awoke in the waters the sea has been a cradle endlessly rocking. The earliest organisms that can be traced are the blue-green algae; fossil re-

Holdovers from Ancient Days

Two sea creatures which have survived almost unchanged from their earliest beginnings are the mollusk called *neopilina (above)* and an odd-looking fish named coelacanth *(right)*. *Neopilina* was thought to have been extinct for 350 million years. However, in 1952 living specimens of the one-inch animal were discovered in an ocean trench some two miles deep. The coelacanth was also believed extinct, but in 1938 live specimens were netted off South Africa. This fish is the world's oldest living higher animal; it probably developed about 300 million years ago. The fish is covered with blue scales and its lobed fins are attached to the body by stalks.

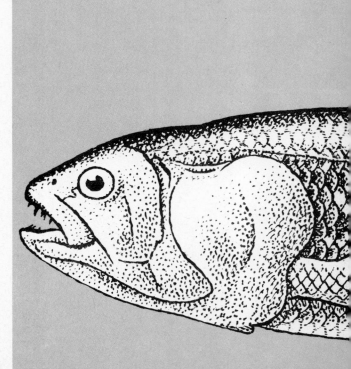

16

mains of these plants have been found in Canada and appear to be at least a billion years old. Yet, plants never evolved very far in the sea. Today, there are fewer than a hundred species of "higher" plants in ocean waters—compared with some 250,000 flowering plants on land.

The story of water-dwelling animals, on the other hand, is quite different. Almost as soon as the jump was made from single-celled to many-celled forms, animals began to show an amazing variety of shapes.

The record of fossils imprinted in rock is our source for the early history of living things. Until a few years ago, such records began with what scientists called the Cambrian period, whose rocks were formed 570 to 500 million years ago. That period was marked by the first appearance of animals with the hard shells that make good fossils. The creatures that preceded them were so soft-bodied that they left comparatively few traces of themselves. Recently, however, at least 130 million years of history were added with the discovery, in England and South Australia, of many impressions left in ancient, hardened mud by pre-Cambrian animals. Through these records we know that some 700 million or more years ago, there were jellyfish (the most primitive creatures to possess mouth and stomach), as well as segmented worms and creatures like flatworms (among the first organisms with a nervous system and brain).

(*Text continued on page 22*)

1 MANTA 20 FT.
2 BLUE MARLIN 10 FT.
3 SAILFISH 8 FT.
4 FLYING FISH 9 IN.
5 SUNFISH 7 FT.
6 OCEANIC BONITO 2 FT.
7 DOLPHIN 4 FT.
8 PILOT FISH 9 IN.
9 WHITE-TIPPED SHARK 7 FT.
10 BLUEFIN TUNA 7 FT.
11 GIANT SQUID 55 FT.
12 SPERM WHALE 60 FT.
13 STERNOPTYX DIAPHANA 2 IN.
14 DIRETMUS ARGENTEUS 2 IN.
15 EEL LARVA 4 IN.
16 HATCHET FISH 1 IN.
17 LAMPROTOXUS FLAGELLIBARBA 8 IN.
18 PLATYBERIX OPALESCENS 3 IN.
19 ROOSTERFISH 15 FT.
20 VIPERFISH 12 IN.
21 PRAWN 4 IN.
22 PHOTOSTOMIAS GUERNEI 7 IN.
23 LANTERN FISH 3 IN.
24 CHIASMODON NIGER 2 IN.
25 OPISTHOPROCTUS SOLEATUS 1 IN.
26 MELANOCETUS JOHNSONI 2 IN.
27 SNIPE EEL 2 FT.

The Fish and Mammals That Rule the Sea

Animals with backbones rule the sea. They differ from all other animals by having a rigid support—the backbone—inside the body. In some primitive sea animals such as the shark the backbone is little more than a tough rod wrapped in elastic tissue. In most fish, however, the backbone is a flexible cord of bones called vertebrae, to which powerful muscles are attached. It is the backbone and the muscles, controlled by a complex nervous system, that have made the aquatic animals the masters of the sea.

The painting above shows fish and mammals that live in a 4,000-foot-deep cross section of the sea; the painting key lists the creatures and their average lengths. Familiar food and sport fish race in the upper waters and burst through the surface. Here too swim the sharks, the 3,000 pound manta ray and a huge ocean sunfish that dwarfs a man. In the mid-depths, a backboned whale, the world's largest animal, battles with a giant squid, the largest animal without a backbone. Still farther down live creatures that are known only by their scientific names. One tiny dweller of the deep can swallow prey larger than itself. In the blackness of the lowest levels only body patterns of glowing color identify friend from foe.

1 SEA COLANDER
2 SEAWEED
3 MUSSEL SHELL
4 EDIBLE MUSSELS
5 PINK-HEARTED HYDROIDS
6 REDBEARD SPONGE
7 RIBBED MUSSELS
8 COMMON SEA STAR
9 RAZOR CLAM SHELL
10 OYSTER DRILLS
11 ROCK BARNACLES
12 IRISH MOSS
13 SEA GRAPES
14 SEA VASES
15 SEA ANEMONE
16 SEA PORK

17 SUN STAR
18 MOON SNAIL SHELL
19 BOAT SHELL
20 DOG WHELKS
21 PERIWINKLES
22 PURPLE SEA STAR
23 CORALLINE ALGAE
24 BLOOD SEA STAR
25 SAND DOLLAR AND SHELL
26 MUD STAR
27 BRITTLE STAR
28 ROCKWEED
29 ROCK CRAB
30 GREEN SEA URCHIN AND
   SHELL
31 SEA PEACHES

32 BAY SCALLOP SHELL
33 JINGLE SHELLS
34 GREEN CRAB
35 HERMIT CRAB
36 SOFT CORAL
37 SEA CUCUMBER
38 PURPLE SEA URCHIN
39 WHELK EGG CASE
40 SKATE EGG CAPSULE
41 LADY CRAB
42 BLUE CRAB
43 TORTOISE-SHELL
   LIMPETS
44 SEA SPONGE
45 EYED-FINGER SPONGE
46 YOUNG HORSESHOE CRAB

The Teeming Life of the Shore Bottom

The painting above shows a few square feet of shallow ocean bottom along the New England coast of the United States. Here sea animals flourish, taking from the splashing water life-giving oxygen and the dissolved minerals that they require to make shells and bones. But there is also danger. Predators, attracted by the abundance of prey, cruise in search of easy meals. Waves and tides tear at the unanchored animal and toss it ashore to die.

Evolution has given the animals that live on the coastal bottoms the equipment to survive these onslaughts. Shallow-water sponges have fingerlike bodies that offer less resistance to the surging waters than do the bodies of the vase-shaped sponges that live in the deeps. The sea stars creep along the bottom at six inches a minute and hold on to the rocks with such a strong grip that their tubular feet will part from their bodies before they will let go.

The wealth of fossils from the Cambrian time that followed offers a much fuller picture of early life. There were no animals possessing backbones and no plant or animal had evolved that was capable of moving out of the sea and onto the land. The sea, especially the sunlit shallows, remained the nursery of life. Animals with protective shells, plates and skins multiplied there. Lamp shells, snails and graptolites (drifting creatures with fantastic branching skeletons) appeared. But the most important forms were the arthropods, something like today's crabs and lobsters. The chief of the arthropods of the Cambrian sea floor was a many-legged creature called the trilobite.

In the Ordovician age that followed (500 to 440 million years ago), the arthropods gave way to giant mollusks called nautiloids, whose shells were up to 16 feet long. Clams, starfish and corals put in their appearance. It was not until the Silurian age (440 to 395 million years ago) that fish—the first animals with backbones—arrived on the scene in abundance. The other great event of the Silurian period was the invasion of the land by the higher plants. This occurred after the emergence of great mountains had the effect of driving the sea back and uncovering low-lying land areas. Soon afterward the first animal, a small sea scorpion, crawled up on the beach and stayed.

By the next era, the Devonian (395 to 345 million years ago), the sea had much the look of today. Fish had multiplied into forms whose kinship to modern fish is obvious. The vastly increased mobility, strength and intelligence of these fish had made them the dominant form of marine life. A few of them followed the scorpion ashore and developed into the first land-dwelling vertebrates (animals with backbones). Man is descended from one of the fish that left the sea.

It was in the periods after the Devonian that life really began to evolve on the land. Of course, it would continue to develop in the sea as well; new types of fish and other forms of marine life replaced older ones. And the boundaries of the sea would change as great sheets of ice spread down from the poles, shifting the borders between land and ocean. But the main drama of life had already moved to a new domain—the land.

The Fiery Birth of an Island

Belching acrid, sulphurous smoke, a volcano erupts from the sea near Japan and creates a new island. This particular island was formed in 1952; other islands have been born elsewhere since then. As volcanoes erupt, their fumes often stain neighboring waters for days and kill great numbers of fish.

2

A Close Look at the Ocean Floor

AN UNDERWATER LANDSLIDE takes place on the ocean floor off the coast of Lower California. Such landslides occur when masses of sand, dumped into the sea by streams and rivers, pile up on the edge of an underwater cliff. Finally, the weight becomes too great and the sand sweeps down the slope.

Although most of our world lies beneath the ocean, until a few years ago man knew less about the ocean floor than he did about the moon. The ideas man had about the vast area beneath the sea were mostly misconceptions based on myths, wrong information and totally baseless beliefs.

Until recently people believed that the ocean floor was more or less flat. But soon after World War I an invention called an echo sounder opened up the undiscovered frontier of the ocean bottom to systematic exploration and mapping. The echo sounder is a device that sends a beep of sound down into the water and then measures the time it takes for the echo to return to the surface; thus technicians can tell by the length of time it takes to receive an echo from the ocean floor how deep that floor lies.

What echo sounding has done is to give us a picture of the bottom of the sea far different from traditional beliefs. It has been found that in the murky realm far beneath the surface there are huge mountain ranges and plunging canyons, towering volcanoes and dizzying cliffs.

We now know that the ocean floor is divided into three great domains. First there is the continental shelf, a shallow border zone between the continents and the sea, crammed with life. Then comes the continental slope, where the land really ends and where the floor plunges suddenly two miles and more to the true ocean bottom. Finally there is the deep-ocean basin.

The continental shelves skirt most of the earth's coasts, sloping gently away from the shore to a depth of about 500 feet. They were once dry land but were drowned by the rising seas as the last great glaciers melted. Discoveries of elephant teeth miles off shore indicate these creatures roamed what is now the dry continental shelf 20,000 years ago.

At the outermost edge of the continental shelves the ocean floor suddenly drops like a roller-coaster track, to fall in an unbroken line for two or three miles. These slopes are among the most spectacular features of the entire earth. Where mountains crowd a coast and there is no gentle shelving, as occurs along the Chilean shore, the drop-off down the slope can be up to five miles from the surface to the bottom of the sea.

At the foot of the continental slopes the deep-ocean floor begins. It is by far the biggest of the ocean's three zones, for it includes five sevenths of the total sea area, one half of the earth's surface. It is in this enormous area that scientists, using advanced devices designed for ocean research, have in the past few years made their most startling discoveries about the earth's surface.

An early surprise came when oceanographers found that many of the peaks, cones, ridges and cliffs that reared from the deep-sea bottom have been preserved unchanged through the ages. On the Pacific floor, for example, there is a cliff a half mile to a mile high and 3,000 miles long. It seems as sharp and jagged as if it had been wrenched from the sea bottom yesterday, and yet it may be as much as one million years old. The reason this cliff looks youthful—in geological terms—is that the forces that wear down the mountains on land do not operate deep within the ocean. Underwater there can be no wind, frost or rain to keep up an unremitting process of erosion.

Many other features of the ocean bottom have also been charted recently. There are

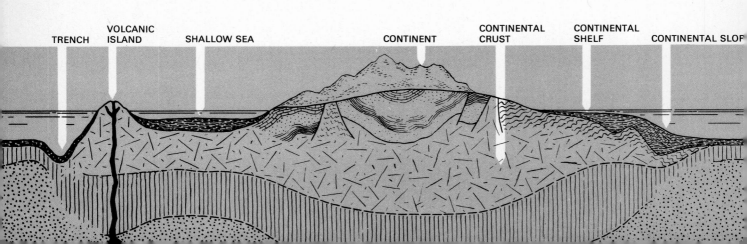

TRENCH   VOLCANIC   SHALLOW SEA   CONTINENT   CONTINENTAL   CONTINENTAL   CONTINENTAL SLOP
          ISLAND   CRUST   SHELF

sizable submerged banks that seem to have been part of the continental land masses at one time but were somehow detached. The most publicized one is the Galicia Bank, a flat-topped bulge that lies in 2,500 feet of water off the coast of Spain. Its location gave rise to guesses that modern science had at last found the fabled lost continent of Atlantis. According to legend, Atlantis, once the home of a rich civilization, sank beneath the ocean after a catastrophic earthquake. However the samples of the soil from Galicia Bank that have been brought up have not given any evidence that air-breathing creatures ever lived there.

Though it may not be possible to discover lost continents, oceanographic studies have yielded information on what has been happening to real continents. Samples taken from the ocean floor off the coast of South America in 1959 revealed a layer of white volcanic ash. This in itself was not surprising, for there are many volcanoes in the sea; what was startling was the discovery that the ash contained granitic materials.

This was unusual because while granite is the basic rock material found on land, it is

Ups and Downs of the Sea Bottom

A cross section through the earth's crust shows different features of land and sea and indicates how the earth's surface undergoes slow, constant change. Molten rock from the mantle of the earth oozes up through the Mid-Ocean Rift (*below and maps, pages 29-37*); in cooling, this rock forms new ocean floor at the rate of one to two inches per year and pushes older sections ahead of it as it spreads to both sides. The ocean floor, made of basalt, supports the continents, which are made of lighter granite, and carries them along like a conveyor belt. This accounts for the slow "drifting" of the continents over the ages.

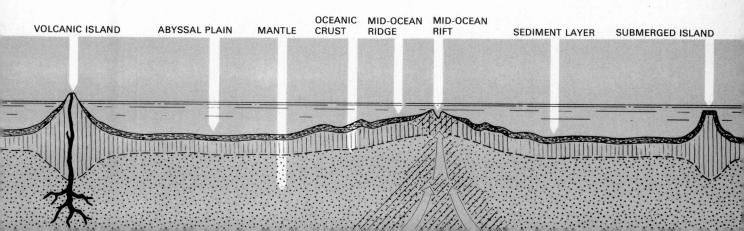

VOLCANIC ISLAND   ABYSSAL PLAIN   MANTLE   OCEANIC CRUST   MID-OCEAN RIDGE   MID-OCEAN RIFT   SEDIMENT LAYER   SUBMERGED ISLAND

not found in the earth's crust beneath the sea. Therefore, a widespread layer of granitic volcanic ash could mean only one thing: sometime in the prehistoric past, there had been a blast from the mountains on land, probably the Andes. Considering the fact that the granitic ash found off the South American coast extended over an area of tens of thousands of square miles, scientists have come to believe that it was deposited by one of the greatest and most devastating explosions the world has ever seen.

Discoveries such as these have helped to make the period in which we live the second great era of discovery, rivaling the 15th and 16th Centuries when much of the surface of the globe was explored. But the most important result of this new age of exploration—the greatest geographical discovery of modern times—is the recognition of the Mid-Ocean Ridge.

Imagine a single connected mountain range 40,000 miles long snaking through every ocean in the world. That is the Mid-Ocean Ridge. Hints of its existence have been accumulated since 1873 when a rise in the middle of the Atlantic was discovered. But the full extent of the ridge did not become known until after World War II. Meanwhile earthquake specialists had begun to notice a peculiar coincidence: their locating equipment fixed the centers of many deep-sea earthquakes at precisely the spots where the already discovered mountains of the Mid-

(Text continued on page 38)

PORTRAITS OF THE OCEAN BOTTOM

A Look at the World with the Oceans Removed

In the past decade or so, scientists from many nations have cooperated to explore in great detail the world's seas. From their findings, cartographer Kenneth Fagg has mapped the earth's floor as it would look if all the water were drained off. These maps are shown on the next nine pages, starting with views of the ice-covered north and south polar regions. The deepest areas are colored red, the next deepest a yellowish tan, the shallowest green. The gray areas are land.

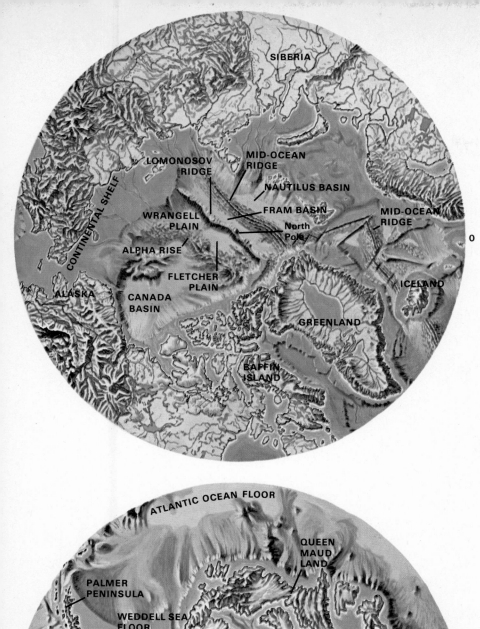

THE ARCTIC, smallest of the earth's oceans, is nearly landlocked. Its Mid-Ocean Ridge, an extension of the Mid-Atlantic Ridge, has been studied by nuclear submarines. Its deepest spot, the Fram Basin, lies 16,835 feet below sea level.

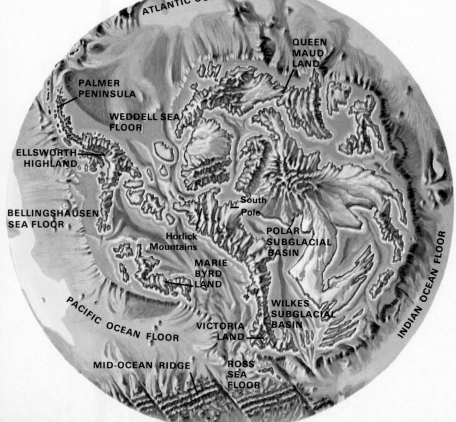

THE ANTARCTIC, largely under ice like the Arctic, is not so much a sea as a continent laced with waterways and divided by a 12,000-foot-deep trough linking the Wedell and Ross Seas. At the bottom of the map is the Mid-Ocean Ridge.

29

Coiling like a giant snake, the Mid-Atlantic Ridge
—an undersea mountain range—is a prominent
feature in this view of the Atlantic Ocean north of the
equator. The continents of Africa and Europe
are at right, and the Americas are at far left.

The 10,000-mile-long ridge, which bisects the
Atlantic, varies in width from 300 to 1,200 miles and
takes up a third of the ocean's floor. It is studded with
live volcano peaks, and is split by a crevasse, or rift,
along its entire length. The ridge surfaces at only a

THE NORTH ATLANTIC

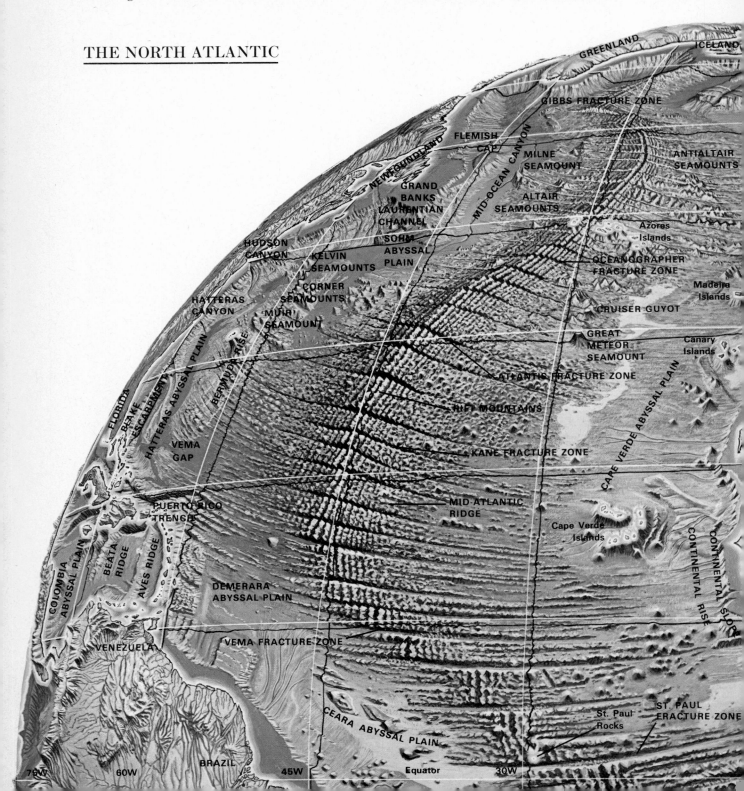

GREENLAND
ICELAND
GIBBS FRACTURE ZONE
FLEMISH CAP
MILNE SEAMOUNT
ANTIALTAIR SEAMOUNTS
NEWFOUNDLAND
MID-OCEAN CANYON
GRAND BANKS
LAURENTIAN CHANNEL
ALTAIR SEAMOUNTS
Azores Islands
HUDSON CANYON
SOHM ABYSSAL PLAIN
OCEANOGRAPHER FRACTURE ZONE
KELVIN SEAMOUNTS
CORNER SEAMOUNTS
Madeira Islands
HATTERAS CANYON
MUIR SEAMOUNT
CRUISER GUYOT
GREAT METEOR SEAMOUNT
Canary Islands
FLORIDA
BLAKE ESCARPMENT
HATTERAS ABYSSAL PLAIN
BERMUDA RISE
ATLANTIS FRACTURE ZONE
CARE VERDE ABYSSAL PLAIN
VEMA GAP
RIFT MOUNTAINS
KANE FRACTURE ZONE
PUERTO RICO TRENCH
MID-ATLANTIC RIDGE
Cape Verde Islands
CONTINENTAL SLOPE
COLOMBIA ABYSSAL PLAIN
BEATA RIDGE
AVES RIDGE
CONTINENTAL RISE
DEMERARA ABYSSAL PLAIN
VENEZUELA
VEMA FRACTURE ZONE
CEARA ABYSSAL PLAIN
St. Paul Rocks
ST. PAUL FRACTURE ZONE
BRAZIL

75W   60W   45W   Equator   30W

few places, among them Iceland, the Azores, and the St. Paul Rocks. The crevasses that run across the ridge are tracks left by the continents as they moved apart. The terraced ridges parallel to the crest are solidified molten rock that came up through the rift and slowly edged away. At both sides of the ridge are bumpy stretches called abyssal hills that slope down into the abyssal plains. The plains lie about three miles below sea level and rise at their edges to meet the continental shelves.

Rockall Island

UNITED KINGDOM

FRANCE

BISCAY ABYSSAL PLAIN

SPAIN

ITALY

BALEARIC ABYSSAL PLAIN

NAZARE CANYON

ABYSSAL HILLS

TURKEY

EGYPT

SAUDI ARABIA

SAHARA DESERT

RED SEA RIFT

CONTINENTAL SHELF

NIGER CANYONS

ROMANCHE FRACTURE ZONE

NIGER FANS

São Tomé Island

GUINEA ABYSSAL PLAIN   0   15E   30E   45E

60W   45W   30W

Fernando
de Noronha
Island

ROMANCHE
FRACTURE ZONE

CHAIN FRACTURE ZONE

BRAZIL

PERNAMBUCO
ABYSSAL
PLAIN

CONTINENTAL RISE

MID-ATLANTIC RIDGE

TRINIDAD SEAMOUNT LINE

VAZ ABYSSAL PLAIN

RIO GRANDE PLATEAU

MID-ATLANTIC RIDGE

ARGENTINE RISE

ARGENTINE ABYSSAL PLAIN

Falkland
(Malvinas)
Islands

FALKLAND ESCARPMENT

SANDWICH
TRENCH

South Georgia
Island

South Orkney
Islands

South Sandwich Islands

THE SOUTH ATLANTIC

The Mid-Atlantic Ridge continues into the South
Atlantic and is the most important feature of this
part of the undersea world. Curving south past the
25,748-foot-deep Romanche Trench, the ridge
broadens and pokes above water in lone peaks such
as Ascension and St. Helna islands. At the
bottom of the map, the Mid-Atlantic Rift swings
around the tip of Africa, becomes the Mid-Indian
Ridge and continues on land as the East African
Rift, finally ending at the Red Sea. The abyssal

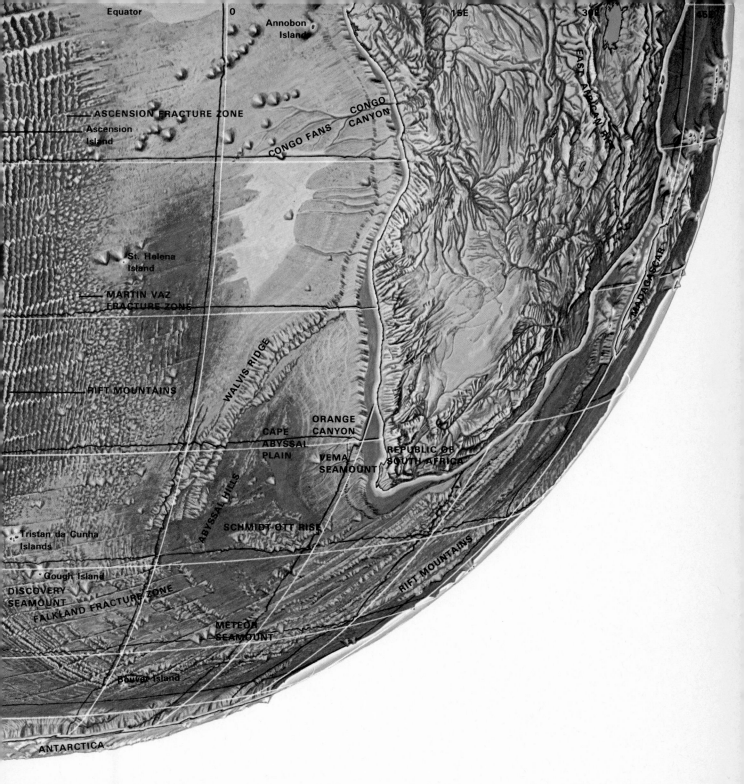

Equator 0 15E 30 45

ASCENSION FRACTURE ZONE

Annobon Islands

Ascension Island

CONGO CANYON

CONGO FANS

EAST AFRICAN RIFT

St. Helena Island

MADAGASCAR

MARTIN VAZ FRACTURE ZONE

WALVIS RIDGE

RIFT MOUNTAINS

ORANGE CANYON

CAPE ABYSSAL PLAIN

VEMA SEAMOUNT

REPUBLIC OF SOUTH AFRICA

ABYSSAL HILLS

SCHMIDT-OTT RISE

Tristan da Cunha Islands

RIFT MOUNTAINS

Gough Island

DISCOVERY SEAMOUNT

FALKLAND FRACTURE ZONE

METEOR SEAMOUNT

Bouvet Island

ANTARCTICA

plains, which flank the Mid-Atlantic Ridge, are the continents' dust bins—the resting place for silt carried from the shores. Sometimes the sediment crashes off the continental shelf in undersea avalanches, which may help carve out canyons like the Congo Canyon. In areas like the Trinidad Seamount Line off Brazil, the continental shelf extends offshore, then drops off in sheer cliffs. Farther south lies the South Atlantic's deepest spot —the 27,114-foot-deep South Sandwich Trench.

33

The Pacific Ocean, whose northern half is shown below, is the largest single feature of the earth's surface. All six continents lumped together would not fill its vast area. The Mariana Trench (*far left*) is a huge hole nearly seven miles deep. Toward the center of the Pacific's great bowl, the volcanic cones of the Hawaiian Islands poke up some 32,000 feet above their base on the sea floor. On the eastern edge, along Central and South America, is the East Pacific Rise, a ridge of undersea mountains

THE NORTH PACIFIC

KODIAK GUYOT

ALEUTIAN TRENCH

GILBERT SEAMOUNT

CHINOOK TROUGH

ALASKAN ABYSSAL

KURILE TRENCH

EMPEROR SEAMOUNTS

MENDOCINO FRACTURE

JAPAN

JAPAN TRENCH

MUSICIANS SEAMOUNTS

MURRA

Midway Islands

SCRIPPS SEAMOUNT

MARCUS-WAKE SEAMOUNTS

BONIN TRENCH

HAWAIIAN DEEP

MOLOKA

HORIZON GUYOT

MID-PACIFIC MOUNTAINS

Hawaiian Islands

TAIWAN

Johnson Island

MAGELLAN SEAMOUNTS

MARIANA TRENCH

PHILIPPINES

SYLVANIA GUYOT

Marshall Islands

Caroline Islands

Palmyra Island

Line Islands

Gilbert Islands

Christmas Island

160 E   165 E   180   165 W   150 W

following the coast of Central and South America. In the north, this ridge runs into the Gulf of California. Several gigantic crevasses split the Pacific from east to west. The largest among them are up to 30 miles wide and nearly two miles deep.

Most of the powerful earthquakes in the North Pacific occur near the volcanic islands that span its western edge; this confirms that the ocean floor is spreading toward the continents, causing these upheavals as it tumbles into deep ocean trenches.

HODGKINS RIDGE
PATHFINDER SEAMOUNT
PLAIN
ONE
GREAT TROUGH
COBB BANK
IONEER RIDGE
MENDOCINO RIDGE
DELGADA FAN
SAN ANDREAS FAULT
MOONLESS MOUNTAINS
ERBEN GUYOT
MONTEREY FAN
RACTURE ZONE
FIEBERLING GUYOT
JASPER SEAMOUNT
Guadalupe Island
GULF OF CALIFORNIA
FRACTURE ZONE
HENDERSON SEAMOUNT
Revilla Gigedo Islands
CUBA
CLARION FRACTURE ZONE
CALIFORNIA SEAMOUNT
CAYMAN TROUGH
MATHEMATICIANS SEAMOUNTS
MIDDLE AMERICA TRENCH
TEHUANTEPEC RIDGE
CLIPPERTON RIDGE
GUATEMALA BASIN
CLIPPERTON FRACTURE ZONE
EAST PACIFIC RISE
COCOS RIDGE
GALAPAGOS FRACTURE ZONE
Equator
135 W
120 W
105 W
Galapagos Islands
90 W

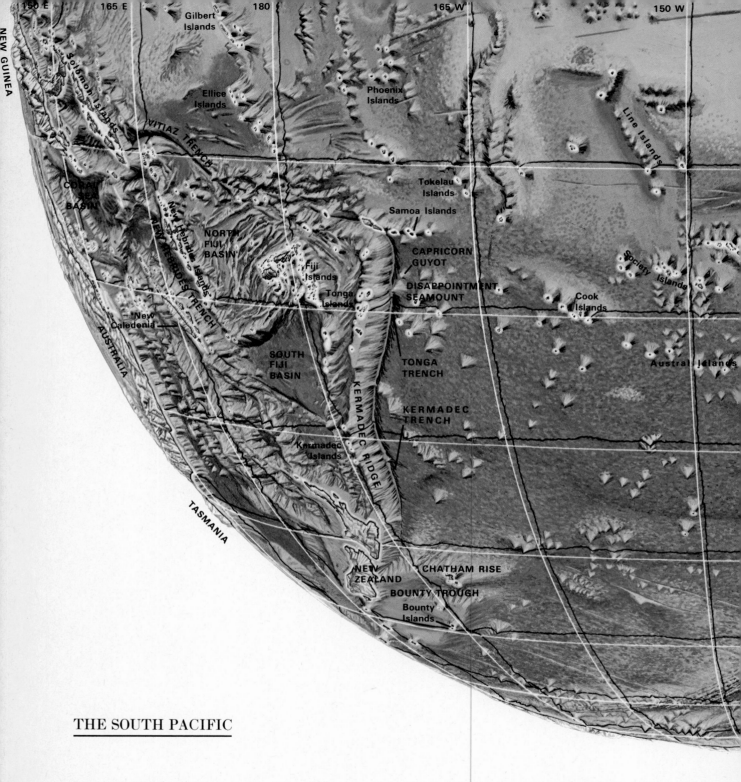

NEW GUINEA

Gilbert
Islands

Solomon Islands

Ellice
Islands

Phoenix
Islands

VITIAZ TRENCH

CORAL SEA
BASIN

New Hebrides Islands

NEW HEBRIDES TRENCH

NORTH
FIJI
BASIN

Tokelau
Islands

Samoa Islands

Line Islands

Fiji
Islands

CAPRICORN
GUYOT

AUSTRALIA

New
Caledonia

Tonga
Islands

DISAPPOINTMENT
SEAMOUNT

Society Islands

SOUTH
FIJI
BASIN

Cook
Islands

TONGA
TRENCH

Austral Islands

KERMADEC RIDGE

KERMADEC
TRENCH

Kermadec
Islands

TASMANIA

NEW
ZEALAND

CHATHAM RISE

BOUNTY TROUGH

Bounty
Islands

THE SOUTH PACIFIC

The South Pacific, an ocean of breathtaking
dimensions, is dominated by the East Pacific Rise
(*right*), a submarine mountain range that is part
of the world-encircling Mid-Ocean Ridge. The rise
leads into the Pacific-Antarctic Ridge and finally

into the Mid-Indian Ridge. Scientists have found
that temperatures above the ridges are five times
more intense than elsewhere on the ocean floor,
due to the molten rock welling up. Another feature
of the South Pacific is the Tonga-Kermadec Trench

GALÁPAGOS
FRACTURE ZONE

Galápagos
Islands

CARNEGIE
RIDGE

EAST PACIFIC RISE

PERU

Marquesas
Islands

MARQUESAS FRACTURE ZONE

BAGEL
SEAMOUNT

Tuamotu
Archipelago

HELEN
SEAMOUNT

NASCA RIDGE

PERÚ-CHILE
TRENCH

San Félix
Island

Pitcairn
Island

EASTER FRACTURE ZONE

Easter
Island

Juan Fernández
Islands

CHILE

GIFFORD
SEAMOUNT

SOUTH
CHILE
RIDGE

PACIFIC-ANTARCTIC RIDGE

ANTARCTICA

(left). It is almost seven miles deep and 1,600 miles long—big enough to hold six Grand Canyons. North and west of it, Soviet scientists discovered the Vitiaz Trench near the area where the U.S. and Japanese fought the great battles of World War II. The rest of the ocean floor is punctuated by seamounts and small coral islands. Scientists have coined some curious names for their discoveries; Disappointment Seamount, for instance, commemorates two sets of lost dredging tools.

Ocean Ridge had been found. In 1956 two scientists, Maurice Ewing and Bruce C. Heezen made a couple of bold predictions. They said that a part of the Mid-Ocean Ridge would be found wherever deep-sea quakes occurred. They also forecast that the ridges would be found to make up a single giant mountain ridge.

Since then, both predictions have proved correct. Equally significant was the discovery of a giant crack running down the center of the entire ridge. This crack is eight to 30 miles wide and more than a mile deep in many places. The great majority of quakes in the sea are centered on this crack.

There are numerous theories about the origin of the Mid-Ocean Ridge and its monster fault. Heezen has startled scientists with his theory that the earth is expanding and that the crack along the entire ridge is the result of this increase in size. Geophysicists who support Heezen's theory have calculated that this expansion of the earth is taking place at an average rate of about one fiftieth of an inch per year. Whether or not this theory is correct for the whole earth, it is certain that the planet is stretching apart at certain places.

The great undersea ridge is just one of the puzzles of the deep. There is still the mystery of the deep trenches. At first thought, it is entirely reasonable to assume that parts of the ocean will be deeper than other parts and that the deepest areas will be those farthest from land. Therefore it is surprising to learn that the deepest trenches are close to shore and are found near certain kinds of land—almost always steep coastal volcanic ranges or chains of volcanic islands. Even more puzzling is the fact that when the trenches are found near islands, they always lie on the ocean side—rather than on the continental side.

The trenches all have very similar "V" shapes and about the same depth—approximately 35,000 feet—though they vary considerably in length. Puzzling over these facts, scientists are beginning to grasp the outlines of a breathtaking idea. Perhaps, these scholars suggest, the trenches have something to do with the way continents grew.

Obviously trenches are formed by some powerful down-dragging force. Some think they began with currents of thick, semi-liquid molten lava beneath the earth's crust that welled up from the hot interior through volcanoes near the present trenches. Then, as it cooled, this mass slid sideways and sank to the ocean bottom. As it sank, the lava could have gouged out a deep V on the ocean floor. This V then gradually filled up with sediment washed down from the coastline or the nearby islands. When the trenches were full—and again for reasons not understood—their bottoms rose again, pushed up by some force from below. This moved the top layers of sediment above sea level to create a new chain of rocky islands near the older volcanic chain. In time, the area between the chains collected enough

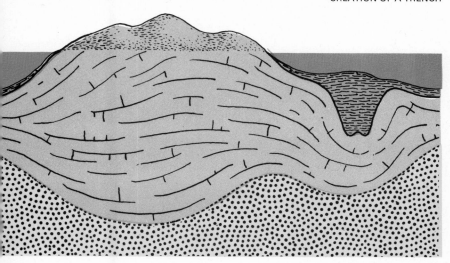

CREATION OF A TRENCH

Birth of an Island

The three sketches illustrate one theory of how land is created. Scientists think a slow current of softened rock flows horizontally through the earth's mantle (*arrow, top*). For unknown reasons the current turns downward, dragging a strip of crust with it. Over millions of years, sediment fills the trench (*center*). Finally, as the current becomes weaker the heavier rock beside the trench slides down (*bottom*) pushing the silt-filled trench up in an arc of volcanic islands.

FILLING OF THE TRENCH

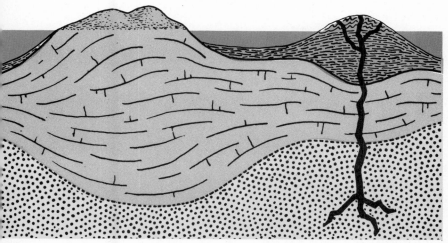

AN ISLAND ERUPTS

39

sediment to form a land bridge, and a new land mass was born.

Heezen's theory that the earth was expanding enjoyed many years of popularity. But subsequently another concept was advanced by the late geologist Harry H. Hess and has won even wider scientific support. The Hess theory states that the ocean floor may actually be moving. This motion causes the deep trenches near the continents. And it may also bring on one of nature's most terrifying acts—earthquakes.

According to Hess the ocean floor moves in this way. Rock, under such pressure that it flows almost like lava, is pushed up from the earth's interior, spilling onto the ocean floor from the gigantic Mid-Ocean Ridge. The rock spreads across the ocean floor, solidifying on top into a crust that advances up to several inches every year. When it arrives at a continental land mass it dips down at a 45° angle, forming a V-shaped trench with the continent's edge.

How does a moving ocean floor cause earthquakes? As the ocean floor dips down, it drags the edge of the continent down with it, creating tremendous tension in the bedrock formation underneath. After a time —perhaps hundreds of years—this continental bedrock cracks under the enormous pressure. With this cracking, the continental land snaps back much as a cork held under water bobs to the surface when it is released. The result is an earthquake.

Most of the more violent earthquakes in the world occur near the ocean, particularly the Pacific. This fact supports the moving-floor theory. Because the floor is dragging down the continental land edges, naturally more earthquakes are caused there.

The Good Friday earthquake in Alaska in 1964 was caused, it is believed, by movements below the surface like those just described. Here, according to the theory, the weight of the rock piled up in the offshore trenches for about a thousand years forced the Alaskan shoreline inward about 65 feet and pulled it down about 15 feet. When the foundation rock cracked, the land bobbed back into balance, causing a great upheaval that wiped out many inhabited places and killed 115 people.

Thus, the ocean floor is constantly renewing itself. New rock pours across it, carrying new material from the earth's interior, only to be covered by fresher outpourings.

Mining the Ocean's Floor

Manganese nodules on the ocean floor more than
three miles down, were photographed by Russian
IGY scientists. One expert estimates that the metal,
essential in the refining of steel, may be present in
such quantities that one square mile of sea floor
contains nodules worth $10 million.

Inset map labels:

B

ATLANTIC OCEAN

NORWAY

LABRADOR

Hudson's Str.

France

Spain

Portugal

MEDITE

Part
of
BARARY

N. England

Virginia

R. S. Laurence

Peninsil

VI
IX
X
XI
XII

Main map labels:

LAND
of the
ESKIMAUX'S or

LAKE MICHIGAN

LAKE HURON

LAKE ONTARIO

LAKE ERIE

Fort
Detroit

Niagara falls

PENNSYLVANIA

NEW YORK

NEW JERSEY

Philadel.ª

NEW ENGLAND

NOVA SCOTIA

NEW
HAMPSHIRE

MASSACHUSETS

CONNECTICUT

Cape Cod

Long. I.

Nantucket I.

St. Georges Bank

Bay of Fundy

St. Laurence

VIRGINIA

MARYLAND

Delaware
Bay

Chesapeak
Bay

Ohio River

NORTH CAROLINA

C. Hatteras

SOUTH CAROLINA

GEORGIA

P. Royal

WEST FLORIDA

EAST
FLORIDA

PART OF THE
GULF of MEXICO

BAHAMA I.

Bermuda I.

ATLANTIC OCEAN

3 Minutes
3 Minutes
3 Minutes
3 Minutes
4 Minutes

3
Currents: Rivers within the Ocean

The waters of the sea are always going somewhere. If you dive into the surf at a beach in Massachusetts, some of the water particles that cling to your back may have just arrived from 9,000-miles-distant Australia after years of travel. The surface waters drift in mighty whirlpools, half an ocean in size. The deep waters creep—in journeys that may take centuries to complete.

This restlessness is almost as much a part of the sea as its wetness. The best way to understand the waters' constant motion is to take a long-range view of what the earth does in space. As it moves through space the earth spins on its axis in such a way that the seas near the equator receive the direct rays of the sun. Consequently they get much more heat than do the polar seas. That fact alone would be enough to set the oceans stirring. When the sun warms the surface water at the equa-

THIS GULF STREAM CHART was drawn in 1770 for Benjamin Franklin to show the course of the mighty current. Franklin had gotten the information from American seamen who rode eastward with the flow to save two or more weeks on a crossing. Eventually all sailors adopted the time-saving route.

Forces That Shape Currents

Three factors affecting the speed and direction of ocean currents are illustrated in the drawings below. In the tropics, the sun's rays strike directly, concentrating a lot of heat in a small area instead of spreading it out, as happens near the poles. As tropic seas warm up, they expand and flow "downhill" toward the poles. The second factor, the earth's rotation, spins the currents in the Northern Hemisphere to the right and those of the Southern Hemisphere to the left. This is the Coriolis effect. These two factors—uneven sunlight and the spinning, or Coriolis. effect—combine to produce global wind belts. These winds blow out of the northeast and southwest in the Northern Hemisphere, and out of the southeast and northwest in the Southern Hemisphere. All three factors produce clockwise surface currents in the Northern Hemisphere and counterclockwise ones in the Southern.

tor, the water expands, and the sea level is likely to be a few inches higher at the equator. This is not much, but it does produce a tiny slope. As a result, the surface water near the equator pushes "downhill" toward the North and South Poles. On the other hand, north and south of the equator the heavier cold water (heavier because water contracts as it cools) sinks below the warm and tends to spread slowly along the bottom toward the equator.

The interchange of warm equatorial waters for cold polar waters is one of the most important of the ocean's movements. However, it is complicated by the sweep of other great forces that are also set in motion by the whirling of the earth.

As the earth spins on its axis it creates a force that works to speed up water along the western shores of the oceans. Nor is that all, for the spin also causes the water to veer

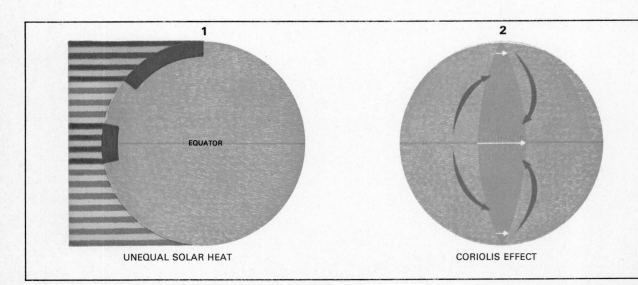

1 UNEQUAL SOLAR HEAT

EQUATOR

2 CORIOLIS EFFECT

slightly to the right in the northern half of the world, toward the left in the southern. This is called the "Coriolis effect," after the Frenchman who first described it.

Another equally important force that produces movement of the waters is the wind —also set in motion by the rotation of the earth. The steadiest winds on earth are those at the edge of the tropics, the trade winds. These blow westward toward the equator in both hemispheres, then wheel northeast and southeast to help drive the currents in both the Northern and the Southern Hemispheres along their great curving routes.

One of the first men to engage in the scientific study of ocean currents and proclaim their importance to mankind was Benjamin Franklin. He noted that American ships commonly took about two weeks less to cross the Atlantic than English vessels. When Franklin asked a cousin, a whaling captain from Nantucket Island, about this difference, he learned that American captains heading for Europe were taking advantage of a current running eastward across the North Atlantic at three miles an hour; on their way home Yankee seamen were piloting their vessels so as to avoid this mighty eastward-flowing current as best they could.

Using this information, Franklin had a chart drawn showing the course of the great river in the sea (*pages 42-43*). At the bottom of the chart, he inscribed the words "Gulf Stream." Franklin's chart, drawn for the use of all ships sailing across the Atlantic (the haughty British skippers ignored it for the first few years), was the first systematic chart of an ocean current ever published.

To this day, the Gulf Stream remains the most intensively studied of all ocean currents. Now, of course, we look upon it as simply part of a single great eddy, or gyre, as oceanographers call it, that extends over the

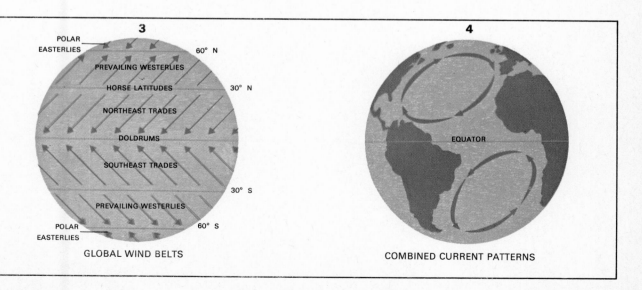

3

POLAR EASTERLIES

60° N

PREVAILING WESTERLIES

HORSE LATITUDES — 30° N

NORTHEAST TRADES

DOLDRUMS

SOUTHEAST TRADES

30° S

PREVAILING WESTERLIES

POLAR EASTERLIES — 60° S

GLOBAL WIND BELTS

4

EQUATOR

COMBINED CURRENT PATTERNS

whole North Atlantic basin. This enormous whirlpool moves in a great clockwise circle off the coasts of the West Indies, North America, southwestern Europe and northwestern Africa before completing the circle near the West Indies.

In the middle of the ever-turning circle of North Atlantic currents is the relatively still region known as the Sargasso Sea. This may be thought of as the hub of the North Atlantic wheel—but a very large hub, measuring something like 1,000 miles wide and 2,000 miles long. Moreover, like most wheel hubs, it sticks out of the plane of the wheel; scientists have calculated that the level of the Sargasso Sea is four feet higher than the water level along the Atlantic Coast of the United States. This "bump" is the result of a variety of causes, one of them being the expansion of the almost still Sargasso waters by the sun's rays.

In the South Atlantic, the North and South

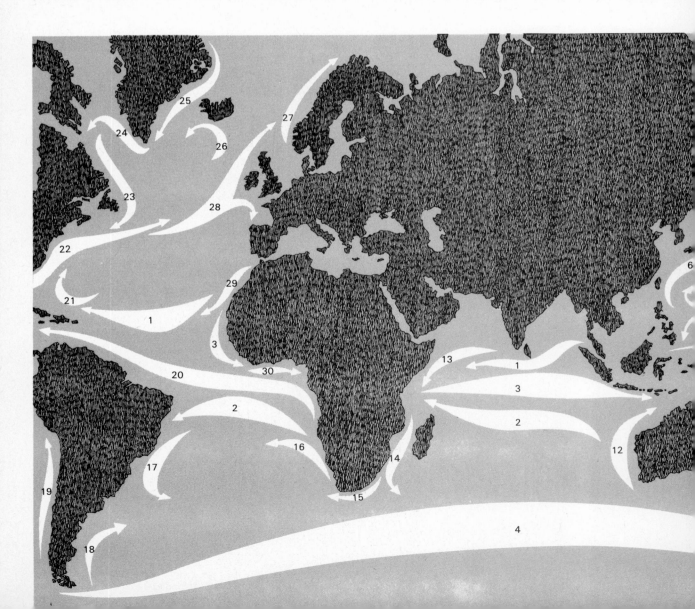

Pacific, and the Indian Oceans, there are similar turning wheels, though not all the circling currents are as strong as in the North Atlantic system. The current wheels of the South Atlantic almost duplicate those in the North, but in the reverse direction; because southern currents are on the other side of the equator, they run counterclockwise.

The northwestern Pacific has its counterpart of the Gulf Stream in the Kuroshio Current. Skirting Formosa and the Japanese islands, this big, slow-drifting stream delivers the same sort of warm, beneficent clouds and nourishing rain showers to the coasts of British Columbia, Washington and Oregon that the Gulf Stream bestows upon the coasts of northwestern Europe.

Oceanographers assure us that these enormous eddies—and the similar but ill-defined circling drifts of the Indian Ocean—are the main currents of the ocean's surface. It took years and years of observation to learn these

Trails across the Sea

Currents—mighty rivers of moving water—cross all the world's seas. Thirty of the major surface ocean currents are mapped at left. Long-term currents, which flow all year long, are pushed along by differences in the weight of water. These differences arise from varying water temperatures and salt content. The currents are shaped by the earth's rotation and prevailing winds and curve when they near land masses. In the days before sail, currents transported migrating people on rafts—a feat duplicated by scientists who floated with the South Equatorial Current across the Pacific on a small craft of balsa.

1. NORTH EQUATORIAL CURRENT	16. BENGUELA CURRENT
2. SOUTH EQUATORIAL CURRENT	17. BRAZIL CURRENT
3. EQUATORIAL COUNTERCURRENT	18. FALKLAND CURRENT
4. ANTARCTIC CIRCUMPOLAR CURRENT	19. PERU CURRENT
5. NORTH PACIFIC CURRENT	20. GUIANA CURRENT
6. KUROSHIO	21. ANTILLES CURRENT
7. OYASHIO CURRENT	22. GULF STREAM
8. ALEUTIAN CURRENT	23. LABRADOR CURRENT
9. CALIFORNIA CURRENT	24. WEST GREENLAND CURRENT
10. FLORIDA CURRENT	25. EAST GREENLAND CURRENT
11. EAST AUSTRALIAN CURRENT	26. IRMINGER CURRENT
12. WEST AUSTRALIAN CURRENT	27. NORWEGIAN CURRENT
13. SOMALI CURRENT	28. NORTH ATLANTIC CURRENT
14. MOZAMBIQUE CURRENT	29. CANARY CURRENT
15. AGULHAS CURRENT	30. GUINEA CURRENT

47

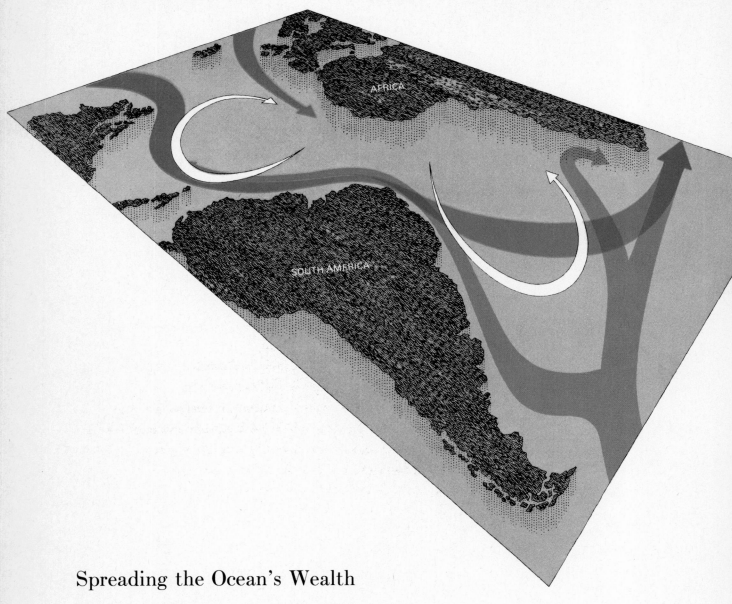

Spreading the Ocean's Wealth

Major currents vital to life in the Atlantic Ocean are
mapped in the diagram above. Deep currents run far
below the surface currents (*white*), which extend
downward only to 2,000 feet. These cold waters from
the poles, rich in oxygen and minerals, flow toward
the equator at depths under 10,000 feet. When the
deep water surfaces—a phenomenon known as
upwelling—it is often along coastlines. Where
upwelling occurs, plankton, a basic food for fish,
thrives; this in turn leads to a large fish population.

SURFACE CURRENTS

ANTARCTIC DEEP CURRENT

ARCTIC DEEP CURRENT

48

facts, and most of them have been gathered since 1855, when a United States Navy lieutenant, Matthew Fontaine Maury, published the first worldwide wind and current charts.

Our knowledge of currents flowing undersea is nowhere near complete. Scientists are just beginning to plot the course of some of the earth's deep waters. One current was discovered almost by accident by the United States Fish and Wildlife Service. A research vessel of the Service was in the central Pacific in 1951, testing a Japanese tuna-fishing technique known as long-line fishing, which involves trailing cables several miles long to which are attached smaller fishing lines that dangle downward. To the astonishment of the scientists, this gear began drifting off to the east instead of to the west. A year later, Townsend Cromwell of the Fish and Wildlife staff made further investigations and traced the drift to a huge and previously unknown current that flows eastward, immediately beneath the west-flowing South Equatorial Current. This submarine current turned out to extend at least 3,500 miles, travel almost as fast as the Gulf Stream and carry nearly half the Gulf Stream's load of water. It has been named the Cromwell Current in honor of its discoverer.

On the heels of the discovery of the Cromwell Current came another, this time in the Atlantic. During the work of the International Geophysical Year in 1957 and 1958 (a cooperative effort by scientists of 66 nations to study both outer and "inner" space), a joint British-American expedition located a sizable current below the Gulf Stream. It was detected at depths of 6,600 to 9,800 feet and was flowing in the opposite direction from the Gulf Stream. Its source and destination have yet to be mapped in detail by oceanographers.

We have already seen that cold water is heavier than warm and tends to sink. Salt, too, can make water heavy. On the whole, the proportion of salt in the open sea stays close to 3.5 per cent. Near melting polar ice, however, the water tends to be less salty because the ice that is melting is nearly fresh. By contrast, the water near ice that is beginning to form will have more than an average amount of salt since the ice that is in the process of freezing leaves extra salt behind in the water. Since this kind of water—both cold and salty—will sink the deepest, the heaviest water is found at the very bottom of the sea. Heavy water of this sort, loaded with salt from beneath the antarctic ice shelf, rides the ocean floor all the way to the equator and across it into the Northern Hemisphere. The ride takes a long time. Some scientists figure that 300 years pass before a bit of cold, salty, deep water goes from the Antarctic to the equator. Others say that it takes 1,500 years. By contrast, a bit of warm, relatively unsalty water may take only a year to make the surface circuit of the North Atlantic wheel.

There are also regions of the sea with strong up-and-down movements. Water will rise toward the surface whenever it meets

49

heavier water. It can also rise from moderate depths to fill a space when surface water is carried away. Such movements are called upwellings. They are vital to the life of the sea and to man; they bring minerals with great nutritional value to the upper layers of the sea, where most marine life dwells. The world's most important fisheries are to be found in areas of upwelling.

Although there are many mysteries about the causes of the tiny variations in temperature and saltiness that set subsurface masses of water in motion, the variations can be spotted and even turned to military advantage. Early in World War II, while conducting antisubmarine-warfare drills off Key West and in the Caribbean, the United States Navy found that its submarine detection devices, called sonar, often failed to detect submarines known to be down below. The difficulty was traced to temperature differences in the water, which bent the sonar's sound wave beams, as light beams are bent in a desert mirage. Temperature inversion—layers of cold water above warm—can bend sonar beams even more sharply.

There are other ways in which a knowledge of how salt can make deep water move has been exploited for military purposes.

During World War II, enemy submarines traveling between the Mediterranean and the Atlantic made use of the fact that in almost completely enclosed arms of the sea, saltiness can vary considerably from the average saltiness of the open ocean. The Mediterranean, for example, has so high a degree of saltiness (3.9 per cent) that it is second only to that of the Red Sea (4 per cent).

The average evaporation from the Mediterranean's surface is about 100,000 tons of water a second. This increases the saltiness and hence the density of the surface water. Particularly during the cool winter months, the heavy surface water sinks and flows westward through the narrow Strait of Gibraltar to spill out into the Atlantic. The water lost to the Mediterranean through this outflow must be replaced, so lighter water from the Atlantic pours back past Gibraltar on top of the salty, outgoing stream. During World War II, German and Italian submarines tried to use these currents to slip past the British blockades at Gibraltar. Turning off their engines to avoid giving their presence away, they hoped to drift in and out of the Mediterranean on the currents. A few actually made it.

A Cold Current Carrying Food

Even birds thrive because of the cold waters of the
northbound Humboldt Current. It is rich in plankton,
which are eaten by anchovies. In turn, the anchovies
feed larger fish as well as sea birds like the cormorants
above. The birds' droppings on nearby islands
are used by man as an organic fertilizer.

4
Waves and Tides: What, Why, How

WIND-WHIPPED SPRAY all but hides a 114-foot lighthouse in Massachusetts Bay as it is battered by a gale's waves. Whether caused by winds or by undersea earthquakes, ocean waves can develop enormous power. Some have crashed on Scotland's shores with an impact of 6,000 pounds a square foot.

Ever since man went down to the sea in ships, the rolling waves have fascinated and awed him. The greenish-blue breakers dancing on the shore fill him with delight; the black storm crests towering over a ship's deck fill him with terror. He reels before those most destructive of all waves, the so-called tidal waves that are loosed by undersea earthquakes. He feels the rhythm of the twice-a-day waves we call tides.

Most of the waves we know best are the work of wind driving against water. The wind makes the water move up and down, but—contrary to appearance—it does not move the water forward very much. When a wave rolls over the sea, the water it disturbs is only momentarily carried forward. Each particle of water stirred up by a wave simply moves forward a bit, then down and back nearly to where it started; meanwhile the wave itself moves on to churn up other water particles. We can see how this works by watching the cork on a fishing line on a quiet day. As a wave approaches, the cork is lifted up by the wave's front slope, carried forward up to the crest, then back again as it slides down the wave's rear slope. When the wave has passed, the cork will not have moved more than an inch or so.

A wave watcher can see waves in their simplest form by tossing a pebble into a pond and watching the even succession of ripples fan out in a circle to the pond's edge. In the open sea, waves are built up in a much more irregular manner. There the wind makes wavelets of all sizes and shapes. They come together, they overtake and pass and sometimes swallow each other. If the wind is brisk, it will blow the tops off small, steep waves, forming whitecaps and heaping small waves together.

The size of waves depends on three factors: the strength of the wind, the length of time it blows and the fetch. Fetch is a seaman's term for the extent of open water across which a wind can blow. A four-mile-an-hour wind will stir up real waves, but only if there is a large expanse of open sea—a long fetch. In a sheltered harbor or cove, that same wind will create only small waves, though they will be closer together than if the wind was in the middle of the ocean. Thus, as a general rule, waves close together cannot get very

A Round Trip to Nowhere

A bobbing cork *(below)* illustrates the most important fact about wave motion: while the shape of the wave does move forward (from left to right in this sketch), each drop of water that makes up the wave remains more or less in the same place. As the crest of a wave approaches, the cork (and each drop of water) follows a circular path as it climbs up the front, reaches the peak, then glides down the rear. When the wave has passed, the cork has not moved more than an inch or two from its starting place.

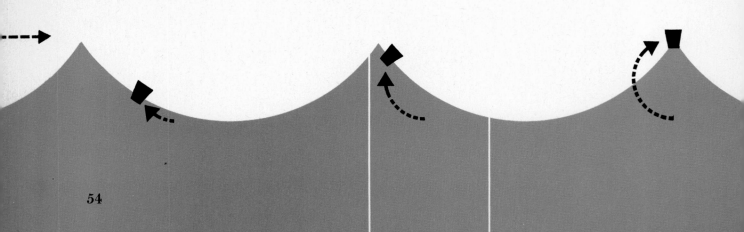

big. This is a considerable comfort to those living on the coast of a narrow bay, for no matter how strong the wind may be, it cannot stir up waves more than a few feet high.

It is on the open sea, where the wind may blow over a fetch of thousands of miles, that the biggest waves have been recorded. The sailor's rule of thumb says that the height of the wave in feet will usually be no more than half the wind's speed in miles per hour. In an 80-mile-an-hour hurricane, by this rule, the waves may run about 40 feet high. But individual waves may be far higher. Whipped together by a storm, traveling at different speeds, several waves may combine to form a superwave that can rise out of the driving, howling sea to flood the biggest ship.

Most stories of big waves are taller than the waves they tell about. But the wave reported in the *Proceedings of the United States Naval Institute* is generally conceded by oceanographers to have topped all others. On February 7, 1933, the United States Navy tanker *Ramapo*, en route from Manila to San Diego, ran into "a disturbance that ... permitted an unobstructed fetch of thousands of miles." To lessen the danger from the stormy seas, the *Ramapo* ran directly ahead of the wind. Soon after midnight the executive officer, Lieutenant Commander R. P. Whitemarsh, saw by moonlight a great sea rising astern "at a level above the main-mast crow's-nest." The *Ramapo* was then on an even keel with her stern in the trough of the sea. From these circumstances and the known dimensions of the ship, Whitemarsh made a simple mathematical calculation that gave the height of the wave: 112 feet.

Despite occasional huge waves, it is the everyday sloshing of the surf that does the sea's main job of shaping the coastline. In the course of a single year, unceasing surf wears down and then rebuilds thousands of beaches, alternately removing and replacing sand in a never-ending cycle. People living on the California coast between Santa Barbara and Los Angeles have seen the surf move great quantities of sand miles along the shore in a few years, robbing some towns of prized beaches and choking the harbors of others with tons of unwanted sand.

The great power that surf has to move sand, together with the many ways in which

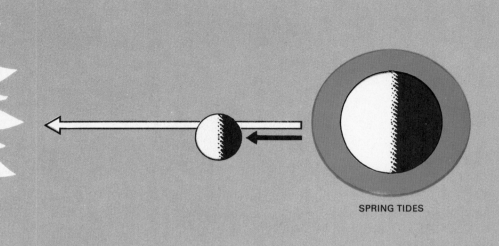

SPRING TIDES

The Pull of Moon and Sun

Tides—the twice-a-day rising and falling of ocean levels—are caused by the gravitational attraction of the moon and the sun. When these two bodies are in line *(above)*, their pulling forces *(arrows)* add together to produce higher, or spring, tides. When the sun and the moon are at right angles, their pulls work in different directions, resulting in less movement of the seas and lower, or neap, tides.

NEAP TIDES

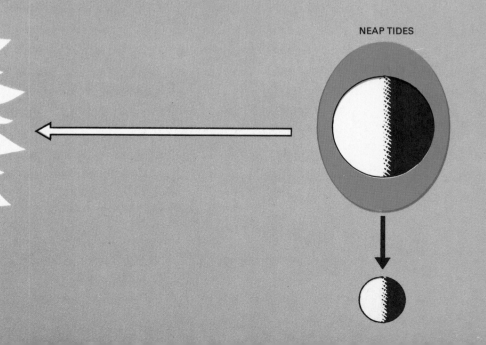

waves and coastal landscape may act together, accounts for the waves' ability to reshape coastlines. Each time a wave passes through shallow water, it lifts loose grains of sand from the bottom. Because the water has been stirred up by the wave, the sand grains are shifted about and settle in slightly different places from before. Such movement of countless millions of sand grains is forever changing the shape and position of beaches.

Along some coasts the shoreline is straight, the underwater slope is uniform and waves often come in directly at the shore instead of at an angle. In such places the surf simply moves sand back and forth from the beach to the underwater slope. During the summer months, fair-weather waves transfer sand from the slope to the beach, laying down a nearly horizontal layer of sand, called the berm, and building the beach outward toward the sea. On some beaches berm can be deposited at fantastic rates: 10 feet in a day, several hundred feet in a season. But it is all temporary. Once autumn storms begin, the sand will be carried back out to sea to the underwater slope, where it will be deposited in the form of winter sand bars.

Of all the waves that wash the world's shores, the twice-daily tides, which rock the oceans in response to the tug of the moon and sun, might seem insignificant at first sight. But the tides unlike the winds, which only roil up the sea's top layers, move the whole ocean. As a matter of fact, they move the earth and air, too. Every time there is a 10-foot tide in the water, the continents rise about six inches and the blanket of air that surrounds the globe bulges out toward the moon and sun to a distance of many miles.

People used to say that the tides represented the breathing of the earth. Now we know that they are caused by the gravitational pull of two neighbors in space, the moon and sun. The moon's pull on the oceans is, of course, much weaker than the earth's own, partly because the moon is smaller than the earth but mostly because it is so far away. Still, this is enough to set all the oceans rocking as the moon swings on its daily journey around the earth. A bulge of water rises on the side of the earth facing the moon. An equal bulge forms at the same time on the opposite side.

The sun, despite its huge size, is so far away that its effect on the tides is about half that of the moon. Nevertheless, the sun alternately adds to and subtracts from the moon's pull, according to the position of the sun. When moon, sun and earth are directly in line—as at the new and full moons—the moon's and the sun's pulls are added together, and we have the unusually high tides called spring tides. When moon, sun and earth are at right angles to each other—as in the moon's first and third quarters—the moon's and the sun's pulls partly cancel each other out, and we have the unusually low tides called neap tides.

But this is not the whole story of tides.
(*Text continued on page 61*)

These contrasting views of the same area result from a 13-foot tide that

creates a lagoon at high tide *(above)*, a muddy flat at low tide *(below)*.

HIGH-TIDE ZONE

PERIWINKLES

MID-TIDE ZONE

MUSSELS

LITTORAL

GOLDEN STAR TUNICATES

Because the oceans do not cover the whole globe evenly but are broken up into many differently shaped basins of varying depths, the water in each basin will slosh back and forth in different ways in respones to the pull of the sun and moon. Tides in the centers of some tidal basins may be slight, and islands in such locations, like Nantucket and Tahiti, generally have tides of little more than a foot.

Tides near the outer rims of particular tidal basins, especially in funnel-shaped bays, where the incoming water has no place to go but up, are apt to be very high indeed. New Brunswick's Bay of Fundy has all these peculiarities, compelling the incoming waters to crowd into a constantly decreasing space. Tides in this bay reach fantastic proportions, surging up more than 40 feet twice a day and sending a four-foot wall of water—the famous Bay of Fundy tidal bore—foaming up narrow, riverlike arms of the bay. All told, each tide carries more than 3,680 billion cubic feet of water into the bay, an amount equal to all the water consumed by all the people of the United States during three months.

When rising tides coincide with storms, they can cause frightful damage, as at Galveston, Texas, in 1900, when a tide rose 15 feet during a hurricane, topped the sea wall and drowned nearly 6,000 people. But the most destructive of all waves are caused neither by wind nor the tug of moon and sun, but by giant disturbances under the sea. These waves have long been called tidal

Life Ruled by the Tides

A rocky seashore (*opposite*) supports marine life of many kinds, each at a depth suited to its needs. In the high-tide zone, which is under water for short periods, are periwinkles, barnacles, brown seaweed and other plants and animals that can live in air for a long time. The mid-tide zone—under water 45 to 85 per cent of the time—teems with mussels, snails, bivalve mollusks and knotted wrack, a seaweed. The bottom, or littoral, generally under water, supports golden star tunicates, seaweed and other life.

61

waves, much to the annoyance of scientists, who point out that the waves have nothing to do with the tides. The scientists have not helped matters by insisting on using the Japanese name for these waves, "tsunami," which means large waves in harbors.

Whether they are called tidal waves or tsunamis, they are caused by world-shaking earthquakes and volcanic eruptions beneath the sea. They cross the ocean in the form of low waves, so low in fact that people on ships at sea often do not realize a tsunami is passing. They flash through the water at jet-plane speed, averaging about 450 miles per hour; individual waves follow each other at more than 15-minute intervals and the first one is not necessarily the worst. When they approach shallow water, they rise to overwhelming heights and hit with unimaginable force. They have been known to rise 60 feet on flat, low-lying shores, and more than 100 feet at the head of V-shaped inlets.

Disastrous tsunamis have struck most frequently on Pacific shores. Japan has had 15 of them since 1596, including one in 1896 that killed 27,122 people. A remarkable series of tsunamis originated in the explosion of the East Indian volcano island Krakatoa in 1883 that killed 36,380 people, wiping out village after village on neighboring islands. Krakatoa's tsunamis went all the way around the world, leaving their mark on tide-measuring instruments in the English Channel.

There is a good chance that such appalling loss of life may be a thing of the past. After 1946 the United States set up a network to flash warnings of undersea earthquakes that might send tsunamis racing across the Pacific. In the tsunami that followed the Chilean earthquake in 1960, many lives were saved when the network's warnings came through in time, but hundreds of other lives were lost, mainly when warnings arrived too late. The tsunami-alert network is now being expanded as other Pacific nations join the United States, and improved arrangements have been made to flash warnings from earthquake recording stations direct to threatened areas. Thus, by taking up still another kind of wave watching, man may learn to live with tsunamis.

From Stones into Sand

Rocks, deposited by glaciers 15,000 years ago, form a Long Island beach. The rocks, ceaselessly pounded by waves, are ground down by two main forces: that of water against stone, and that of stone against stone in the tumbling of the surf. Eventually, these two forces will turn this stony pile into a soft, fine sand.

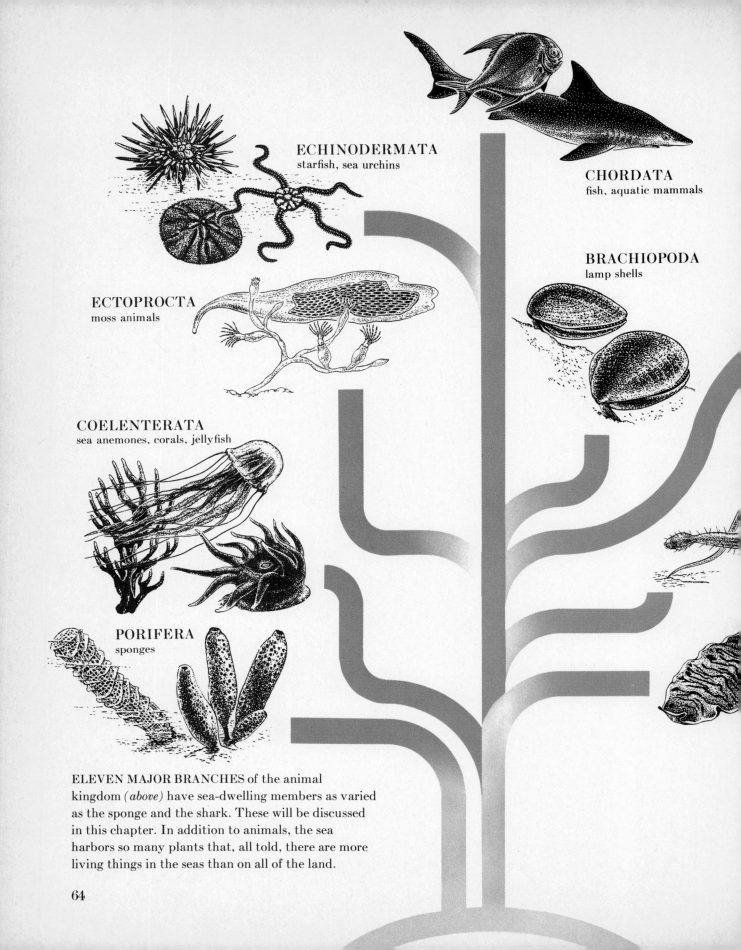

ECHINODERMATA
starfish, sea urchins

CHORDATA
fish, aquatic mammals

ECTOPROCTA
moss animals

BRACHIOPODA
lamp shells

COELENTERATA
sea anemones, corals, jellyfish

PORIFERA
sponges

ELEVEN MAJOR BRANCHES of the animal
kingdom (above) have sea-dwelling members as varied
as the sponge and the shark. These will be discussed
in this chapter. In addition to animals, the sea
harbors so many plants that, all told, there are more
living things in the seas than on all of the land.

MOLLUSCA
clams, snails, octopods

ARTHROPODA
crabs, shrimps, barnacles

ANNELIDA
segmented worms

ASCHELMINTHES
roundworms, rotifers

PLATYHELMINTHES
flatworms

5

The Great Pyramid of Marine Life

In its abundance, its variety, its oddity, its beauty, life in the sea is rich almost beyond imagining. The sea's inhabitants range from the trillions upon trillions of creatures so small they cannot be seen by the naked eye to the 100-foot-long, 150-ton antarctic blue whales, three times larger than any dinosaur. They include some of the loveliest forms that nature has ever created—wonder-

ful fish that are all silver, animals that bloom
like flowers while rooted to the ocean floor,
glowing corals that spread in gorgeous terraced steps along tropical coasts. There are
also worms that grow 90 feet long, fish and
shrimp that feed off tiny animals attached
to larger fish, even fish that can change to
any of eight different colors.

The sea is a good place for life. It is also a
great place for leftover life—jellyfish, corals,
sponges, starfish, horseshoe crabs and other
ancient forms that still flourish although
they reached the limits of their progress long
ago. As a place to live, the sea surpasses the
land in several important ways—less change-
able temperatures, more support against
gravity's pull and, of course, more water
than anywhere else on earth.

Two main facts govern the way sea creatures live: the unbelievable number of marine life forms and the utter ruthlessness
with which the larger creatures eat the smaller ones. It was once estimated, for instance,
that if all the eggs laid by codfish were
hatched and grew to maturity, the Atlantic
would be packed solid with codfish within
six years. But nature does not let this happen. Only a tiny fraction of codfish eggs
ever become full-sized cod, and the same can

PLATYHELMINTHES

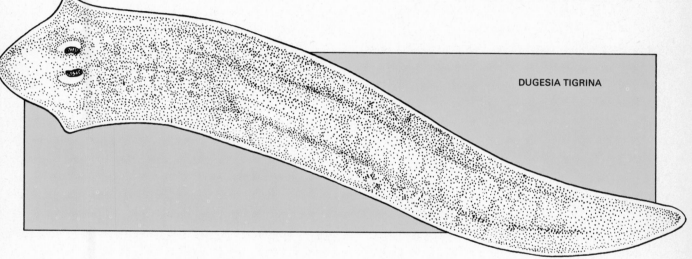

CHARACTERISTICS: (1) Flattened body; (2) gut with single opening; (3) no body cavity. Flatworms, both those that live independently and those that live as parasites on the outside or inside of other animals, make up this phylum. Although Platyhelminthes such as tapeworms may reach 60 feet in length, most, such as the *Dugesia tigrina*, are under half an inch. Members of this phylum live in salt and fresh water and on land.

DUGESIA TIGRINA

be said for other fish. Only one sea creature in about 10 million escapes a violent death. Most of the rest meet their end inside another creature.

The community of life in the sea can be compared to a pyramid. At the base are the trillions of plants and animals so small that they can be seen only through a microscope. These support a smaller number of slightly larger living things, which feed on them; and these, in turn, are food for a still smaller number of yet larger creatures. Finally, at the top of the pyramid are the relatively few large fish and other big sea creatures that

could not exist without all the other layers in the pyramid.

A single example, given by N. J. Berrill in his book *You and the Universe*, reveals just how many lives and deaths are involved in the process of feeding just one humpbacked whale. This sea mammal "needs a ton of herring in its stomach to feel full—as many as five thousand individual fish. Each herring, in turn, may well have six or seven thousand small crustaceans in its own stomach, each of which contains as many as one hundred and thirty thousand diatoms. In other words, some four hundred billion yellow-green diatoms sustain a single medium-

PORIFERA

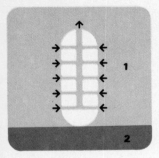

CHARACTERISTICS: (1) Body structure is filled with openings through which flows water that contains life-sustaining food particles and oxygen; (2) stationary as adults. Sponges, which make up the Porifera phylum, are the most primitive of all many-celled animals, having neither true tissues nor organs. Sponges vary in sizes from a quarter inch to six feet and in shape from the vaselike tufted sponge to the bushlike sponge called dead men's fingers.

sized whale for a few hours at the most."

It is now known that there is life even in the deepest and darkest corners of the sea. But a look at all oceanic life shows that most of the sea's living creatures are found in three main areas: (1) the sunlit surface waters of the sea, inhabited by a seemingly infinite number of microscopic drifting plants and animals; (2) the shallow bottom near the shores where worms, shellfish and innumerable other motionless or crawling forms swarm; and (3) the open sea, just beneath the surface waters, which is the home of free-swimming fish.

The best place to begin examining life in the sea is in the surface waters, for that is

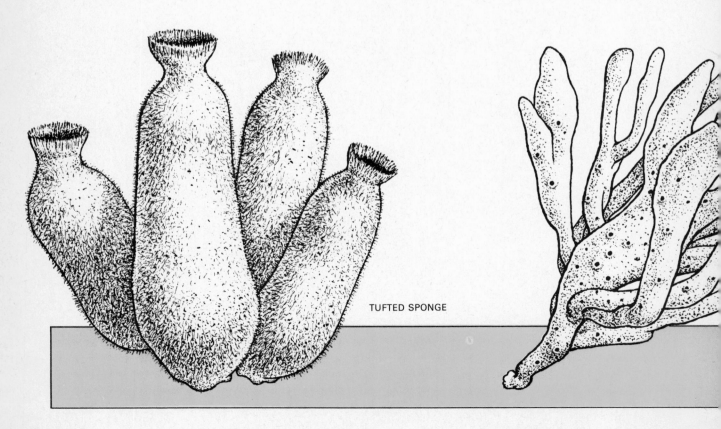

TUFTED SPONGE

where the broad base of the pyramid of life is found. At sea, as on land, the animal kingdom depends on the plant kingdom for food. Plants alone capture the energy of sunlight and use it in making the sugars, starches and proteins that animals live on. Although large visible plants, the seaweeds of the shores, play their part in supplying food, it is a relatively insignificant role; in fact, more than 99 per cent of all plant life in the sea consists not of what most of us would recognize as plants, but of microscopic particles floating in the upper 100 feet or so of the ocean, where they can get light and energy from the sun's rays. Though they cannot be seen with the naked eye, they are there in uncountable numbers, suspended in the water like the motes of dust we sometimes see floating in a shaft of sunlight.

These living specks belong to the layer of marine life called plankton. Plankton includes all the sea organisms, both plant and animal, that are too small and weak to do anything but drift on the currents. Most plankton are only about a thousandth of an inch around.

The most important of these specks are the single-celled algae known as diatoms. Each diatom is enclosed in a clear case that looks like the world's smallest pillbox. Under a microscope, one droplet of sea water

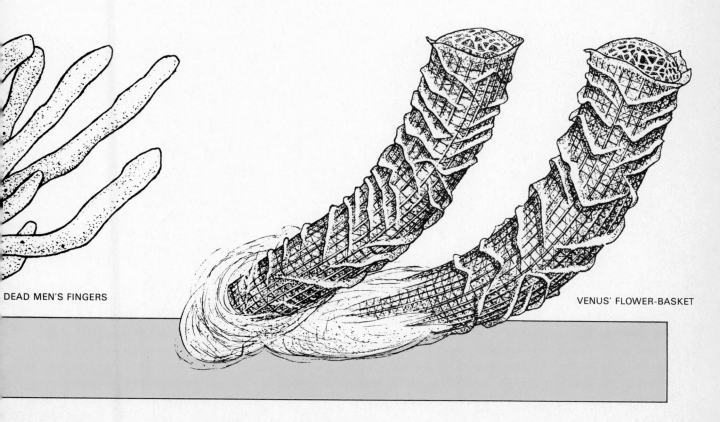

DEAD MEN'S FINGERS

VENUS' FLOWER-BASKET

69

COELENTERATA

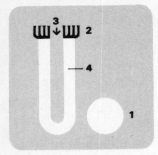

CHARACTERISTICS: (1) Radial symmetry; (2) tentacles with stinging cells; (3) gut with one opening; (4) no body cavity. Jellyfish and sea anemones (*right*), corals and the Portuguese man-of-war are all members of this phylum. Most coelenterates live in salt water, and range from seven feet to less than an inch. Coelenterates such as the jellyfish are free-floating, while others, like the sea anemone, are stationary as adults.

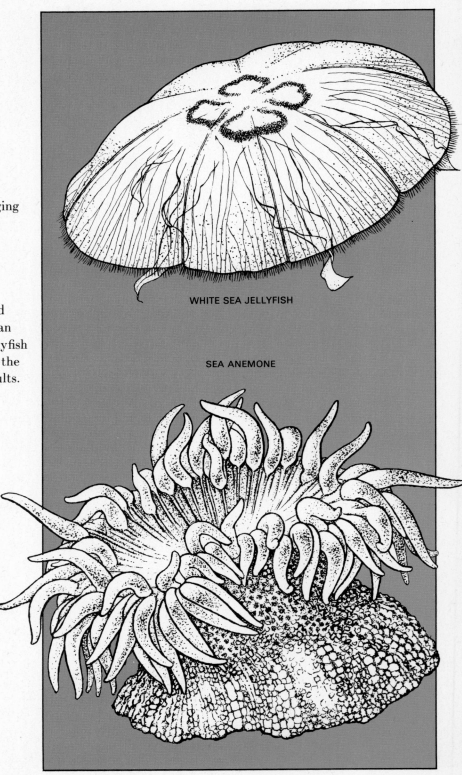

WHITE SEA JELLYFISH

SEA ANEMONE

turns into a dazzling show of diatoms shaped like tiny flashing bracelets, pendants, needles and anchors. Each creature builds its case from the minerals in the sea around it.

Just as land plants depend on minerals in the soil for their growth, these tiny sea plants depend on the salts and minerals in the sea. In the spring the oceans, having been deeply stirred by winter storms, bring to the surface a supply of bottom water enriched with nutritious salts and minerals. These nutrients, together with the increasing hours of sunlight, permit the diatoms to reproduce with astonishing speed. In as little as two days they may double their numbers and spread a living carpet over great areas of the ocean. Hundreds of square miles will be tinged yellow or brown or green, as the sea takes on the hues of the tiny grains of color contained in each plant cell. Soon, however, the supply of minerals dwindles and the population explosion among diatoms comes to an end, but by then other marine life has eaten its fill of the tiny plants.

In the thick of this planktonic soup, there are also swarms of equally small representatives of almost every major division of the animal kingdom. In addition there are things that are neither plant nor animal but something in between. Typical plant-animals are dinoflagellates, one-celled living specks that, like animals, use tiny tails to move through the water but that, like plants, manufacture their own food. Some dinoflagellates are capable of giving off an eerie glow of light called luminescence. When the wind sends a ripple of dancing light through the water on a warm summer night, or a splashing oar and a moving boat trails a dimly glowing wake, it is dinoflagellates that give off the light. You cannot see them, but you can see the light—a chemical reaction touched off in these animals by the disturbance in the sea around them.

In those seasons when plankton thrive, they are devoured by swarms of tiny, shrimplike animals called copepods. Copepods, the smallest of the shellfish, are probably the most numerous multicelled organisms in the world. Usually they are no larger than a pinhead; still, they are a prime food source for larger creatures, from the smallest sardines to the biggest whales.

No one knows how many living creatures of all kinds drift in the plankton layers of the sea. No net has been made that is fine enough to catch the smallest creatures, yet maneuverable enough to trap the swiftest. However, a single quart of surface water may hold several million diatoms alone. Even larger plankton, like krill, the two-inch-long shrimplike shellfish of the Antarctic that blue whales eat, exist in incredible numbers. One scientist has calculated that during the six months a young blue whale spends in antarctic waters, it eats up to some 500 tons of krill. He also estimates that each year antarctic waters spawn a billion and a half tons of krill—that is, 1,100 trillion of these planktonic creatures.

ECHINODERMATA

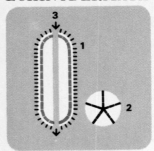

CHARACTERISTICS: (1) Internal skeleton with spines often protruding through skin; (2) radial symmetry —usually with five parts; (3) gut with two openings. Familiar sea creatures such as sea stars, sea urchins and sand dollars belong to this phylum. Echinoderms are salt-water bottom dwellers; they have hundreds of small, tubular feet that not only aid them in moving, getting food and breathing, but even act as sensory organs. In size, echinoderms range from half-inch sea stars to yard-long sea cucumbers.

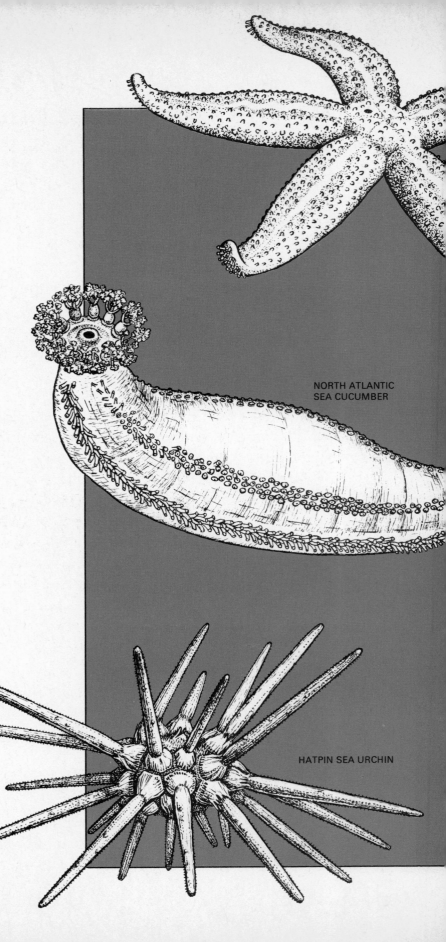

NORTH ATLANTIC
SEA CUCUMBER

HATPIN SEA URCHIN

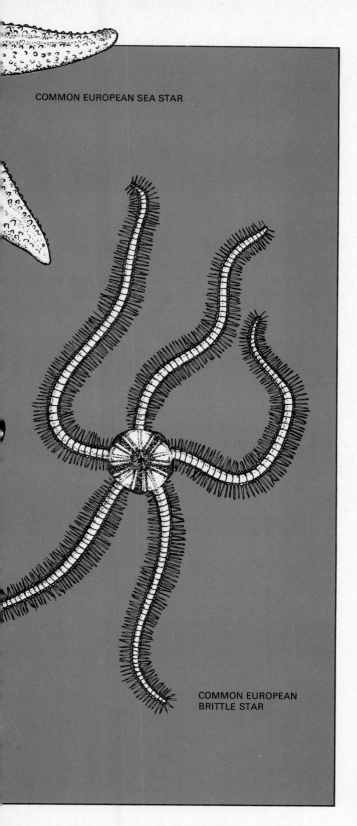

COMMON EUROPEAN SEA STAR

COMMON EUROPEAN
BRITTLE STAR

The second great zone of life in the sea is the shallow bottom along the shores. There, where sunlight can reach all the way down, the thick mass of plankton extends right to the bottom. The coastal shelf is also the one place where plants grow from the sea floor, thereby adding to the food supply for other living things.

The food supply at the bottom of these shallow seas, in fact, is so rich that all the inhabitants have to do is simply open their mouths and eat. Here the main problem is finding a place to anchor and wait for food to drop. Just how enormous a population can get was shown a few years ago when British scientists made a count of a single kind of bottom dweller, the brittle star, a cousin of the sea star. From samplings in an area off England's south coast, they calculated that there were 250 million brittle stars per square mile.

In this great world of plenty the rules are: eat, reproduce and be eaten. The lowly sea urchin has a hard, filelike structure in its mouth that is so strong that it enables the urchin to bite off bits of rock to which algae are clinging. Other creatures have drills for boring holes through mussel shells to eat the animals inside. The scallop has 30 to 40 eyes that can see such danger coming and alert the creature to move away to safety. The clam, however, must rely on its ability to bury itself in the mud on the bottom and then extend a long tube in search of food. If danger threatens, the clam pulls in its tube

ASCHELMINTHES

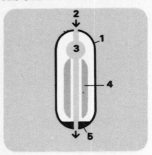

CHARACTERISTICS: (1) Body covered with tough sheath; (2) gut with two openings; (3) distinct gullet; (4) body cavity; (5) adhesive glands that enable the body to cling to solid surfaces. This is a varied phylum whose members are often wormlike. Some Aschelminthes are a foot long, but many are invisible to the naked eye. Their range is varied too; echinoderellas live in coastal waters, *Ascaris lumbricoides* in soil, and still others in fresh water.

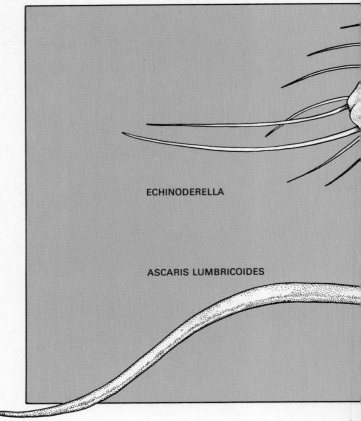

ECHINODERELLA

ASCARIS LUMBRICOIDES

and digs deeper into the safety of the mud.

All kinds of amazing creatures, large and small, inhabit the shallow bottoms, eating the food that falls there—or eating the eaters. In sandy areas, worms burrow through the bottom, poking about in search of morsels that might have slipped down past the massed mouths above. On muddy bottoms, sea cucumbers glide along, slowly scooping the organic slime into their mouths and licking their stringy fingerlike projections, like boys eating jam.

Beyond the continental shelves, where the ocean floor falls away to greater depths, life thins out quickly. As the water beneath the surface of the sea gets deeper, the sunlight becomes less intense and the plants become fewer. Where the sunlight fades entirely, life itself comes almost—though not quite—to a complete halt. Only scavengers live in the lower depths, depending entirely upon bits of organic matter that drift down from above. The rich life of the ocean bottom ends with the limits of the continental shelves.

The third great realm of marine life is found in the wide areas of the open sea, just beneath the surface layer of plankton. In the early days of life in the sea all creatures drifted in the ocean's upper layers or crawled

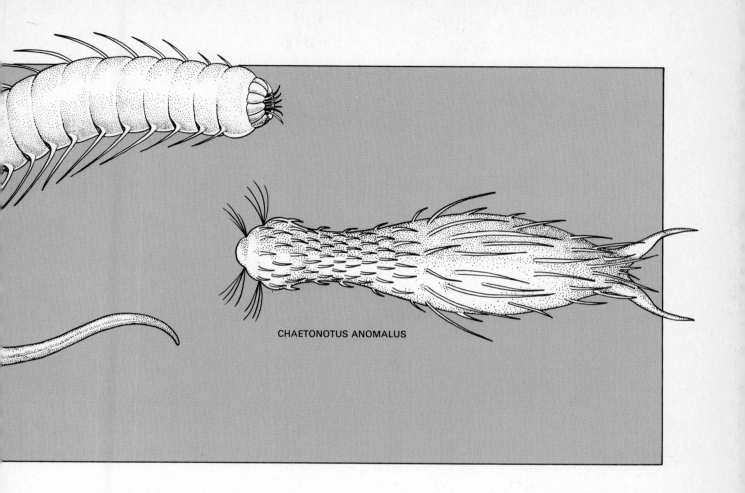

CHAETONOTUS ANOMALUS

along the bottom. The vast space in between was not and could not be occupied by the types of life that existed then. The open sea was not used until a new kind of marine animal evolved, big and strong enough to move about in the open waters regardless of the tides and currents. Today the open sea belongs to those streamlined, neckless, water-breathing, backboned animals called fish.

Fish probably evolved in the shelter of rivers and lakes and only later came down to the sea. Whales, dolphins and a few other mammals, descendants of land animals, have joined them, and marine turtles and even a few snakes also live in the ocean. But only a handful of creatures without backbones, such as the squid and the larger octopuses, live among the fish. Otherwise, the open sea belongs to the bony fish. They far outnumber their primitive fish cousins, the sharks and rays, which have skeletons of an elastic tissue called cartilage instead of bone.

Though there are more than 20,000 species of bony fish, counting both sea and fresh-water forms, they all have a similar basic design. Nearly all open-sea fish are colored to correspond with the waters they live in. Because the sea from above looks blue or green, those are the colors of their backs.

75

ANNELIDA

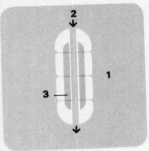

CHARACTERISTICS: (1) Segmented body; (2) gut with two openings; (3) body cavity. Leeches and earthworms are among the prominent members of this phylum, which includes animals that range in size from less than an inch to over three yards. These live in soil, all types of water and in sandy shores. The clam worm belongs to a marine class that dwells on the ocean floor. The snail leech, a member of a mostly fresh-water family, has suckers that enable it to attack other animals and feed on their blood.

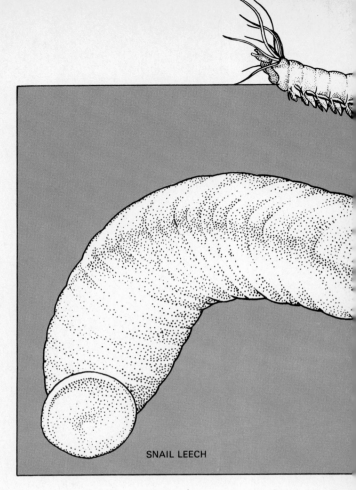

SNAIL LEECH

Because the surface waters from below look silvery or whitish, those are the colors of their undersides. This coloring usually enables fish to blend in with their surroundings and so escape being seen by their enemies.

Most open-sea fish are marked by the torpedo shape that allows them to move most efficiently through the water. Some fish are extremely fast swimmers: sailfish, for example have been clocked at 50 miles per hour, and at least for short distances marlin and tuna can move even faster. Tuna can swim steadily at a speed of nine miles per hour and are, in fact, never motionless. It has been estimated that in 15 years of life a tuna would have swum a million miles.

A few fish, like the one-ton cartwheel-shaped ocean sunfish, the stiff-bodied deep-sea boxfish and the fancier little goldfish rely on their fins to move them forward through the water. But the typical ocean fish uses its fins just for steering, steadying and stopping. Its entire body and tail, driven by one long series of muscles, flip side to side to scull it through the water; it gets extra power and speed by pumping water through its gills to help push it ahead.

A fish has highly developed organs of sense and control. Although nearly every fish possesses eyes, these are of limited use in the water's dim light and are supplemented by

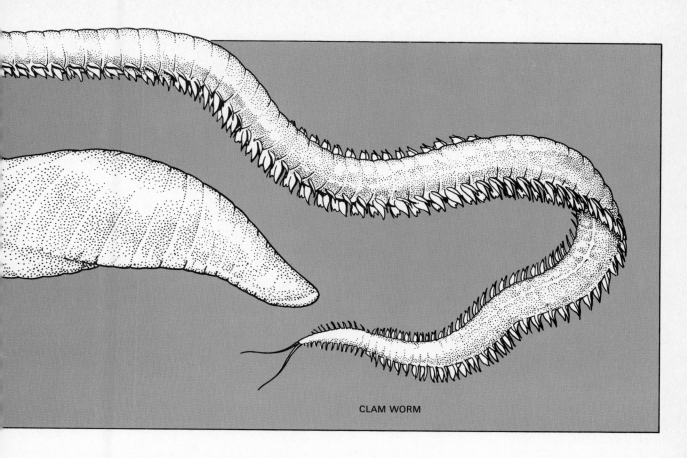

CLAM WORM

other kinds of detectors. Along each side of a fish's body there are special spots, arranged in rows called lateral lines, that are sensitive to pressure and sound. These help guide the fish by informing it of changes in the surrounding water. In addition, most fish have small organs called statocysts, inner cavities, lined with delicate hairs, that contain some loose objects like a few grains of sand. The statocysts are balancing organs that tell a fish, even in darkest waters, whether it is right side up or upside down.

Though the pull of gravity is far less bothersome to sea creatures than to land dwellers, the bones and muscles of fish are heavier than water. Therefore the fish still have to do something to keep from sinking to the sea bottom. Mackerel, tuna and some others seem to stay afloat by swimming constantly. Others, like a common mid-ocean variety, the cyclothone, have layers of lighter-than-water fat that buoy them up. Most fish, however, are kept from sinking by a swim bladder, an organ like a small balloon that is filled with gas drawn mostly from oxygen in the fish's bloodstream. But these air tanks, unlike those of a man-made submarine, cannot be quickly filled or emptied as the fish moves up or down. In this one respect, the man-made submarine is more efficient than the fish. Because of this relatively rigid swim bladder, most fish caught

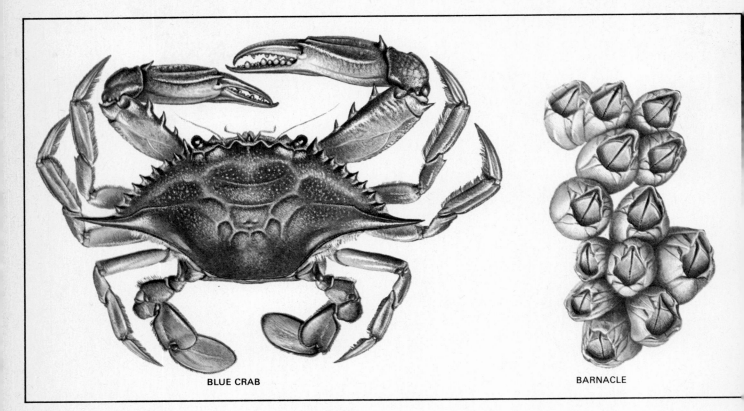

BLUE CRAB

BARNACLE

at depths of more than 60 feet or so are dead when hauled to the surface: the reason is that the rapidly lessening pressure of the water on the swim bladder makes the bladder expand until it pushes against and breaks the fish's internal organs.

Although fish have no vocal organs, they are by no means silent. During World War II, ships equipped with sensitive underwater listening devices reported hearing all sorts of strange beeps, grunts and groans. At first the Navy thought the noises came from other ships. Investigators later found, to their astonishment, that marine animals were responsible, that in fact the underwater world is quite a noisy place.

Fish make sounds by grinding their teeth or by vibrating certain organs such as the swim bladder. Some of the croaks are believed to be mating calls, others seem to be warning signals passed back and forth among members of a school of fish. Commercial fishermen have tried to take advantage of these sounds by lowering listening devices over the sides of their boats in order to locate schools of fish. But most of the commercially valuable fish proved to be the most silent. Furthermore, all species have a tendency to keep quiet when they are in the vicinity of a boat.

Since fish have no eyelids and have to keep moving to stay balanced, scientists have never been able to discover much about how fish sleep. The habits of some

ARTHROPODA

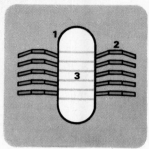

CHARACTERISTICS: (1) External skeleton formed of a hard substance known as chitin; (2) jointed legs; (3) segmented body. Arthropods account for some 80 per cent of the animals of the world. They live in the sea and air and on land. In the sea they are represented by the familiar crabs and barnacles, lobsters and shrimp; but these aquatic members of the phylum are vastly outnumbered by the land insects that make up the bulk of this grouping.

fish indicate that they do indeed sleep. The wrasse, for example, appear to bed down at night; at least they cover themselves with sand and retire. Flounders and sole often lie flat on the sea floor and could probably sleep there. Other fish can wedge themselves in the crevices of underwater rocks for the night. And there are surface swimmers that sometimes seem to rest on floating clumps of seaweed. But as for such open-sea species as the tuna, nobody seems to know if they ever really fall asleep.

Another unanswered question is whether fish age physically as they grow older. Some scientists think that when an animal stops growing it begins to deteriorate, or age. These scientists suspect that in some aqua-tic animals growth never really stops. In that case fish would not age as man does, but would slowly get bigger and bigger. However, it is impossible to test this theory at present, because the eat-and-be-eaten rule of life in the sea gives almost no fish a chance to survive to "old" age. And any fish that is not eaten apparently dies sooner or later because of disease.

It has already been noted that fish of the open sea vary surprisingly little in form from the basic streamlined torpedo shape. But for fish, as for everything else, sur-roundings dictate form. Thus many of the fish that do not live in the open sea but in-stead inhabit tropical coral reefs or sandy

ECTOPROCTA

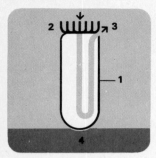

CHARACTERISTICS: (1) Stiff outer covering, often boxlike or vaselike; (2) crown of tentacles; (3) U-shaped gut; (4) stationary. These microscopic animals are plentiful in coastal waters. The boxlike outer covering is attached to rocks, algae, pilings and to other animals. Ectoprocts have no organs to carry food, gases and wastes; instead, they use their body fluids for these purposes.

ELECTRA

shores have taken on startlingly different shapes that suit their special worlds. The sea robin has immense front fins on which it "walks" across the bottom, feeling for hidden mollusks and crabs to eat. The flounder starts life as a pancake standing on its edge, with an eye on each side and a mouth in front. But as it grows, it becomes a horizontal pancake. Its mouth twists around toward the bottom and both its eyes wind up on top. Thus it can sift the sand with its mouth as it searches out food, and simultaneously keep a sharp lookout for enemies above.

Many bottom-living fish are able to change their color and thus blend in with their surroundings. Their skins are equipped with cells that can either reveal or conceal the various bits of pigmentation, or color, to show the tone that best matches the bottom they are resting on. This is not a sign of fish intelligence, for the reaction is automatic, set off in some fish by nerves, in others by chemicals called hormones.

Although the greatest masses of marine life are found near shore and in the sunlit surface waters of the sea, there is a vast area of darkness beneath the surface inhabited by both deep-dwelling animal plankton and the fish that feed on it—and each other. These fish are quite thinly scattered through the depths because food is scarce down there, but the area they live in is so

80

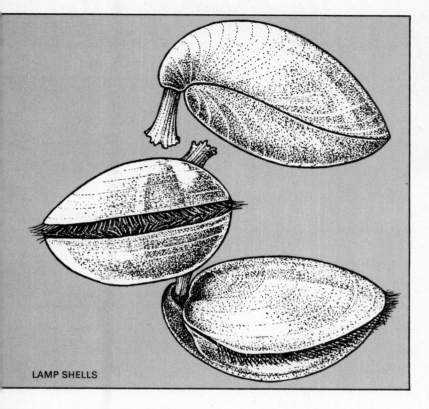

LAMP SHELLS

BRACHIOPODA

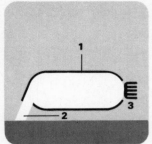

CHARACTERISTICS: (1) Double shell, with dorsal half typically larger than the ventral; (2) stalk, present in most species, attaches to a hard surface beneath the mud; (3) tentacles, used for gathering plankton. Lamp shells belong to this phylum, though they resemble many mollusks (*following page*). Brachiopods live in all the world's seas, and range in size up to three inches.

great that their total numbers are enormous.

The fish of the depths are an odd-looking collection. Unlike silvery surface fish, they are usually dark in color: red, brown, or black. Skeletons are light, tissues fragile and muscle layers thin. These fish must depend on something other than powerful swimming to find food and survive, and they have huge mouths, equipped with long needlelike teeth. Anything they can get their teeth into is a possible meal. One species, the viperfish, has such long teeth that they extend outside the mouth even when its lips are closed. Other deep-water fishes have expandable stomachs, permitting them to swallow victims larger than themselves.

Finding mates in the unlit depths is diffi-

cult. One species has solved the problem with a strange arrangement. The six-inch male is attached to the three-foot female, the two fish sharing one digestive system. Others can make their own light—in the manner of fireflies—and use these lights to recognize mates and potential enemies. So many bottom dwellers are luminous that even the deepest waters are not entirely black, and most fishes have kept their sight.

Fish travel in order to find food or to find a suitable place to lay eggs—which in fish is called spawning. Bluefin tuna follow a regular route each year, only part of which is now known. They spawn somewhere south

(*Text continued on page 84*)

MOLLUSCA

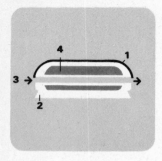

CHARACTERISTICS: (1) Shell made of matter containing calcium, under which is a mantle of tissue. Squid and octopuses, however, have only an internal shell remnant; (2) ventral, muscular foot; (3) gut with two openings; (4) body cavity. Clams, oysters, snails, octopuses, squids—all these animals are but a small part of this large phylum. Mollusks are found in all waters and on land. They vary in size from small snails and scallops to octopuses and 55-foot Atlantic giant squids.

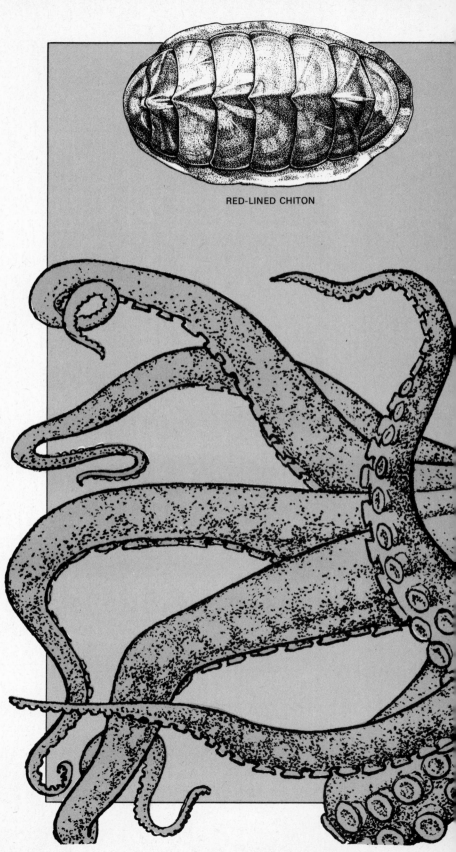

RED-LINED CHITON

MANTLE SCALLOP

ELEPHANT TUSK SHELL

LESSER OCTOPUS

of the Bahamas and arrive in the Gulf Stream in May thin and hungry, weighing about 400 pounds apiece. Eating as they swim, they reach Nova Scotia in September, by which time they weigh 700 pounds. This startling growth has been proved by catching the same fish twice, first in the Bahamas, where it is weighed and tagged with an identifying marker, then in the North Atlantic, where it is weighed again.

An even more remarkable journey is that of eels. Each fall these fish leave European rivers and head across the Atlantic to gather in a small area of the Sargasso Sea near Bermuda. There they spawn and die. When the eggs hatch, the young are caught up by the Gulf Stream and, in a journey that takes three years, float around the great North Atlantic current circling to the coast of Eu-

rope. Developing all the while, the eels reach the mouths of European rivers just when they are ready to begin life as fresh-water creatures. Ten years after, these fish in turn head downstream and out through the ocean to the Sargasso Sea.

It is all the more puzzling that other eels, which seem identical with the European eels, arrive off Bermuda from America to spawn, and in due course the offspring somehow find their way to American, rather than European, rivers after a mere six-month trip along the Gulf Stream. What inborn clock starts them on their journey, what inborn compass guides them, remains beyond our understanding, and the journeys of eels remain a most mysterious episode in the great drama of life and death in the sea.

CHORDATA

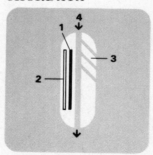

CHARACTERISTICS: (1) A flexible supporting rod, the notochord; (2) hollow, dorsal nerve tube; (3) gill slits; (4) gut with two openings. (In one group, the vertebrates, which include man, (1) and (3) are present only in unborn individuals.) The Sargassum fish (*right*) is a member of this phylum, which ranges from simple organisms to complex mammals.

6

Sharks and Other Terrors of the Sea

ROWS OF JAGGED TEETH in the mouth of a sand tiger shark give it a fearsome appearance. Though sharks stare coldly with fixed eyes, they rely on an acute sense of smell to locate food. All sharks are meat eaters, but only some species—including, on occasions, the sand tiger—will attack man.

On a warm day in May 1959, Albert Kogler and Shirley O'Neill, both 18 and both students at San Francisco State College, decided to cool off with a swim in the Pacific. Splashing into the surf at Bakers Beach near San Francisco's Golden Gate, they swam seaward some 50 yards, Kogler in the lead. "I heard him scream," Miss O'Neill said later. "I turned around and saw this big gray thing flap up into the air. There was a threshing in the water. He screamed again. "It's a shark—get out of here!"

Looking down on the scene from the cliff-top ramparts of the Presidio, the United States Army post, Master Sergeant Leo P. Day watched the struggle with the shark. "I could see the boy in the foaming red water, shouting and signaling someone to go back, go back. Then I saw the girl, swimming toward him with frantic strokes, completely ignoring his warning."

Miss O'Neill reached for Kogler's hand. "But," she recalled, "when I pulled I could see his arm was just hanging by a thread." So she put her arm about Kogler's back and started for shore. She dragged him close enough for a nearby fisherman to throw a

line and pull them both the rest of the way.

His body half drained of blood, the young man died two and a half hours later. From the teeth marks experts identified the attacker as a great white shark. For what Sergeant Day called "the greatest exhibition of courage I have ever seen," President Kennedy awarded Miss O'Neill the 1961 Young American Medal for Bravery.

The full extent of the danger posed by sharks has been widely recognized only in recent decades. A World War II training book, which the United States Navy issued to men serving in shark-infested areas, said that the shark was not much of a menace to man. And an article in a national magazine debunked the shark and portrayed it as cowardly—easy to scare off with a shout or a swat on the snout. Both publications were in error; among the few human-eating sea animals—including barracuda and moray eels—sharks are the worst.

Each year sharks kill or maim several dozen human beings. In one place alone—the

waters along Australia's East Coast—there have been more than 200 shark attacks on humans in 150 years. In 1959, scientists reported 36 unprovoked attacks around the world, 13 of which resulted in death. Of the 36 attacks, 10 occurred in United States waters; three of these caused death.

Sharks are such dangerous creatures because, in fearful and amazing ways, they combine a primitive physical development with a superb adaptability. Three immense groups of muscles that run from head to tail

Death of a Man-Killer

Fatally speared, a hammerhead—one of the most notorious of the man-killing sharks—thrashes about in its death throes (*left*). Only after a long fight is this powerful fish weakened enough for the hunter to approach in safety (*above*). Found in all tropical waters, the hammerhead has a unique T-shaped head that gives it the sinister look of a prehistoric beast.

SHARK

PORPOISE

provide most of the sharks' motive power, and they have taller tails and broader fins than most fish. Their brains are tiny—seldom over three inches long even in large sharks. But they are so tough and durable that it often seems they will never die. Whalers tell of sharks that have been caught, disemboweled and thrown into the water; these gutted beasts then swam straight to whales tied alongside the ship and began tearing at the flesh.

Sharks seem to be almost insensitive to pain, but this does not mean that they lack highly developed senses. Their sense of smell is so delicate that they are nicknamed the "swimming nose"; they can detect blood or a dying fish hundreds of yards away in the water. Experts had long thought that sharks' eyesight is poor and that they do not depend on it. But when an investigator put blinders on captive sharks at the Lerner Marine Laboratory in the Bahamas, they demonstrated their reliance on the visual sense by crashing head-on again and again into walls before

learning to navigate by using their fins to feel their way.

The shark has very unusual teeth. Its mouth is literally studded with several sets of needle-sharp teeth, one row in back of another. These are loosely set in the jaw, and when the front ones break off or wear out, the spare teeth work their way forward to replace them. Shark bites have an unmistakable crescent shape and are often so deep that a major artery is severed. Many victims die from loss of blood before they can be taken to the shore.

Sharks will swallow anything: sea turtles, sea lions, birds, fish, cans, lobsters, horseshoe crabs, garbage, coal, people. One shark captured off an Australian dock had in its stomach half a ham, several legs of mutton, the hindquarters of a pig, the head and forelegs of a bulldog with a rope tied around its neck, a quantity of horseflesh, a piece of cloth and a ship's scraper. Another caught in the Adriatic, had an even stranger bellyful: three overcoats, a nylon raincoat and an automobile license plate.

SWORDFISH   MANTA

Not all of the 250 or so species of sharks are equally dangerous to man. Some are only a foot long. Others, like the dogfish, common in East Coast waters of the United States, have never been known to bother swimmers. Two—the basking shark and the whale shark —are harmless although they reach a length of 30 to 50 feet and are the largest creatures in the sea except for whales. These two giant sharks are plankton feeders, lacking the teeth needed to attack man.

The true killers, experts consider, belong to a dozen species ranging in size from five to 25 feet. Much the most dangerous of these is the great white shark, a fast-moving, powerfully muscled brute that sometimes weighs nearly four tons. Great white sharks, according to one English writer, display "a vast greediness after human flesh." They have attacked American bathers as far north as Cape Cod along the Atlantic Coast.

Another fierce variety, the hammerhead, has a weird T-shaped head that looks like a hammer, apparently helpful as a kind of

A Sign of Danger

A dark, triangular fin slicing through water has traditionally meant the presence of a shark. Less hazardous sea creatures, though, also jut parts of their bodies (*dark-colored areas*) into the air when they swim close to the surface. The porpoise exposes a portion of its back along with its fin. The swordfish shows both fin and tail. The manta, which gives the appearance of two sharks swimming side by side, is actually exposing parallel wing tips.

rudder for rapid turning. At least two of the proved 1959 attacks in United States' waters were blamed on hammerheads. They are bottom feeders that lurk close to shore and along coral reefs, where they are a constant danger to skin divers.

The largest group of man-killers has the fitting name of requiem sharks. By far the most common of the group is the tiger shark, a striped species feared equally in the West Indies and Australia. Also common is the lemon shark, a smaller scavenger with a yellowish belly containing a digestive fluid supposed to be so powerful that, when dropped on a man's hand, it can burn the skin. No one has yet tested this bit of folklore, but it is probably no more true than the mistaken idea that a shark must roll over on its side in order to bite.

Sharks occur in nearly all climates; there is even an arctic species, the Greenland shark. However, the vast majority of sharks are found in temperate and tropical seas, and nearly all shark attacks on humans have taken place when the water temperature has been over 70° F. Some people think that shark attacks take place when temperatures are high because it is only when water is warm that people go swimming. However, recent studies indicate there is more to it than this: shark appetites seem to go up and down with the water temperature.

Sharks have been known to swim considerable distances up rivers in search of prey. They have attacked Indian pilgrims in the Ganges many miles from the ocean, and sharks have bitten men, women and children in an Iranian river 90 miles from the sea. In one of the attacks in Iran, a British driver had driven his ambulance into the water to wash it. He was standing in only a foot of water when struck and he nearly lost a leg.

No one fully understands what makes one shark rip into a man, another circle uncertainly and another turn indifferently away. After more than 100 undersea shark encounters, Jacques-Yves Cousteau, author of *The Silent World* and expert on undersea life, has come to two conclusions: "The better acquainted we become with sharks, the less we know them; and one can never tell what a shark is going to do."

The most effective device yet found for protecting swimmers in shark-infested areas is what Australians call "meshing." Loosely hanging nets are set in place overnight in the water around the bathing beaches. These nets entangle sharks, which are then killed, thus reducing the number of sharks in the area. The nets were first tried at the big beaches near Sydney in 1937, and in just over a year they caught 1,500 sharks, 900 of them probably man-eaters. Since then the catch has dropped to 200 a year, and the number of attacks on bathers at meshed beaches has fallen to zero.

Aside from the shark, the most dangerous salt-water fish is probably the great barracuda. Sleek, cigar-shaped, four to six feet long, this species is more feared than the

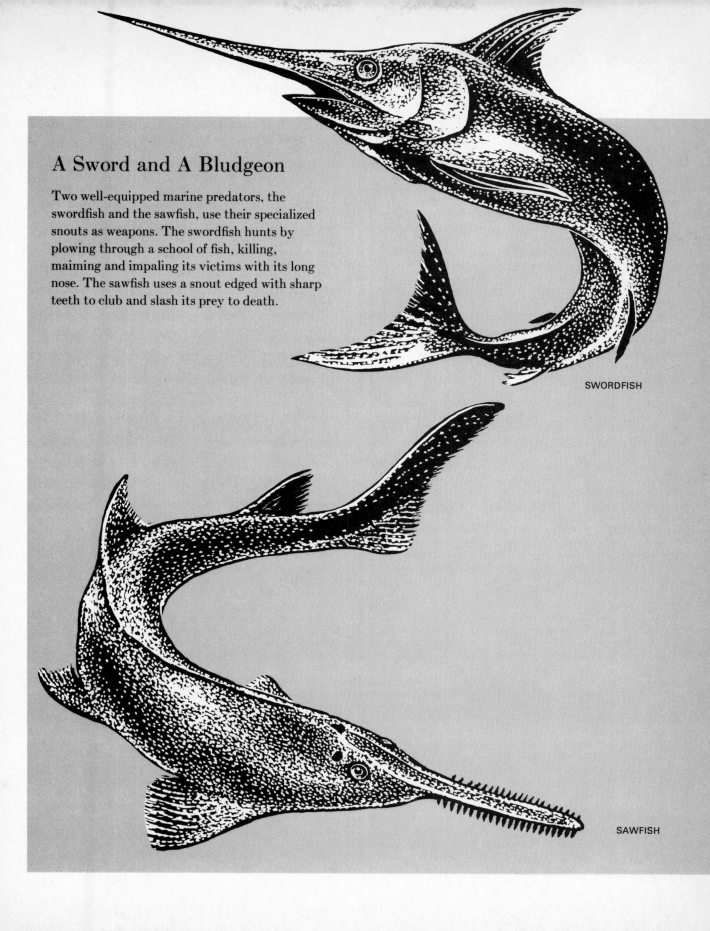

A Sword and A Bludgeon

Two well-equipped marine predators, the swordfish and the sawfish, use their specialized snouts as weapons. The swordfish hunts by plowing through a school of fish, killing, maiming and impaling its victims with its long nose. The sawfish uses a snout edged with sharp teeth to club and slash its prey to death.

SWORDFISH

SAWFISH

shark by many Florida and West Indian divers for two reasons: in the first place, barracuda outnumber sharks in those warm, reef-studded waters; in addition, even when they do not attack a swimmer, barracuda have the unnerving habit of inquisitively following him around. Barracuda have sharp eyesight and they are attracted by bright, flashing objects, by legs dangling from rafts, even by waders along the beach. When a barracuda strikes, it leaves a clean, straight-line wound, utterly unlike the ragged tear left by a shark. In almost a century there have been fewer than 20 attacks that can be charged to the great barracuda. But there have probably been other attacks by these ravenous fish that for one reason or another have not been recorded. In general, however, the attack of a barracuda is much less likely to be fatal than that of a shark because the barracuda does not press its attack.

Moray eels, the fierce-looking, thickset creatures of tropical reefs, are dangerous to man in only one respect. A diver who pokes a hand into a hole occupied by a moray eel may get bitten. Furthermore the eels are very strong and they will not let go; a man grabbed by a moray may drown before he can pry himself loose. But the eel's grasp is purely defensive, and is seldom a serious menace to man.

Of the mammals of the sea, two are known to be real killers. Luckily man rarely runs into either of them.

One potential man-eater is the 30-foot killer whale. This fierce beast ranges in all seas, particularly in the higher latitudes, hunting in packs of a few up to 40 individuals, devouring penguins, fish, walruses and seals.

The other menacing marine mammal is the sea leopard, a 12-foot-long antarctic seal that preys on smaller seals. But it also hunts other warm-blooded animals, and a sea leopard nearly caught a member of the Shackleton Antarctic Expedition of 1914-1915. First the seal lumbered across the ice after him, then dived into the water and swam under the ice, following the man by the shadow he cast on the ice. Finally it burst out again on the frozen surface in front of the man as he ran for his life. The man was saved only when another member of the party heard him yelling, ran up and shot the sea leopard.

A Community with One Body

The Portuguese man-of-war consists of hundreds of individual animals joined together for cooperative living. Divided into four specialized groups, one type makes up the saillike float; another forms the tentacles with their deadly sting; a third type digests food; the fourth is the reproduction center.

7
The Mammals That Dwell in the Sea

A SURFACING WHALE may look like an enormous fish, but it is actually a warm-blooded mammal that must breathe air frequently to stay alive. Like many whale species, the gray whale (*left*) was nearly exterminated by whalers by the 1930s. Now protected, its numbers have climbed from 100 to over 5,000.

A seagoing cow sounds like a foolish idea, yet there is an animal called a sea cow that lives in the water and is a closer relation to the grazing cow than it is to any fish. And the sea cow is just one of many mammals that have returned to the oceans, from which their most remote ancestors crawled hundreds of millions of years before.

One group of these mammals of the sea, the whales, have found the oceans so friendly that in the last 50 million years they have grown not only into the largest mammals but also into the largest animals ever to live on our planet. They are even bigger than the giant dinosaurs that once roamed the earth. Another kind of seagoing mammal, the seal, has become the most numerous group of large meat-eating mammals on earth.

From these facts it would be easy to conclude that the mammals of the ocean are doing very well nowadays. Unfortunately this is not so. At least it has not been so for the last 150 years. For another and even mightier mammal, man, has been giving the mammals of the sea a very bad time.

There is a simple reason for this. Marine, or ocean-living, mammals have the misfortune to be swimming storehouses of products man wants: fur, oil, meat. Even so, they might not be so badly hurt by man if they did not, like man, reproduce so slowly. Every year man takes more than 40 million tons of fish from the oceans without seriously depleting this valuable source of food. The same cannot be said for the slow-breeding mammals of the sea, many of which have been all but stamped out to serve man's needs and desires.

The sea otter, for example, is a handsome creature with one of the world's most valuable skins. At the beginning of this century the sea otter's luxurious dark fur brought prices of $1,700 a skin; to gain this rich prize, men hunted the animal, which had been common from Oregon's Pacific Coast north to Alaska, until it almost disappeared. Laws now protect sea otters, and they survive in small numbers in the Aleutian Islands and along the California coast.

Of all the mammals that now live in the sea, sea otters remain closest in form to the mammals of the land. Sea otters are the only ocean mammals that still have true hind legs. These are short, with webbed toes, and they are specialized for swimming but they are not flippers.

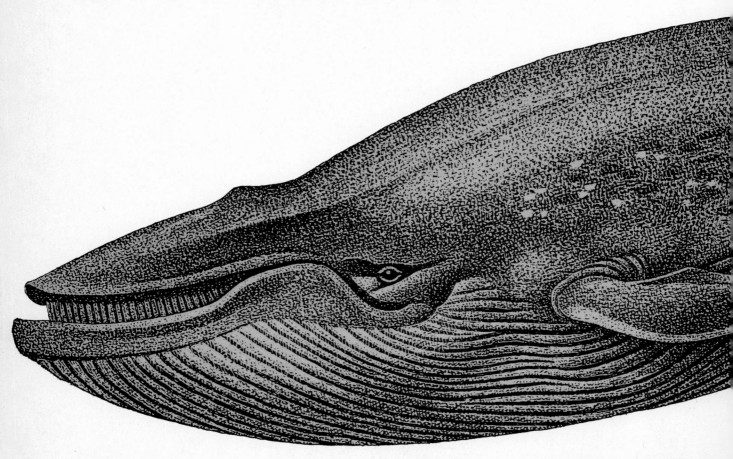

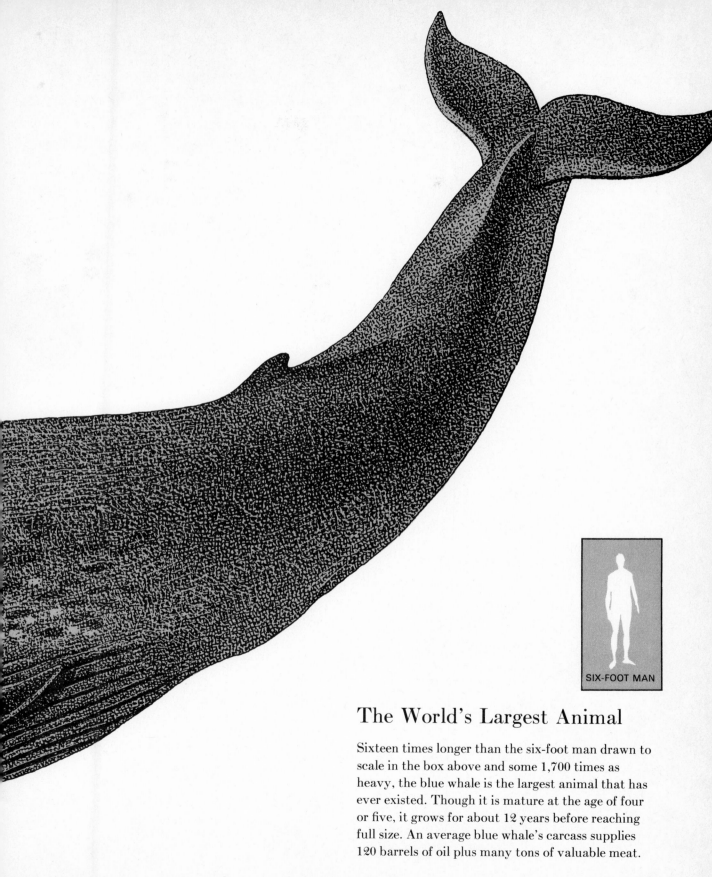

SIX-FOOT MAN

The World's Largest Animal

Sixteen times longer than the six-foot man drawn to scale in the box above and some 1,700 times as heavy, the blue whale is the largest animal that has ever existed. Though it is mature at the age of four or five, it grows for about 12 years before reaching full size. An average blue whale's carcass supplies 120 barrels of oil plus many tons of valuable meat.

HUMPBACK WHALE

SPERM WHALE

Sea cows, on the other hand, are much more obviously built for life in the ocean. These 6-to-10-foot, almost hairless creatures have flippers instead of forelegs and have lost their hind legs altogether. Their place in the mammalian world is puzzling, but naturalists think they may be distantly related to elephants. They form another group that has suffered heavily at the hands of man. Some 150 years ago, the heaviest species of

sea cow—the 30-foot, three-and-a-half-ton Steller's sea cow that lived in the Bering Sea, off Alaska—was wiped out by whalers, who hunted it down for its flesh. Now only two kinds of sea cow survive: the dugong of the Indian Ocean and the manatee of tropical American and African waters.

Manatees are plant eaters and lounge sluggishly in the water of river mouths and along coasts, where their food grows. They breed

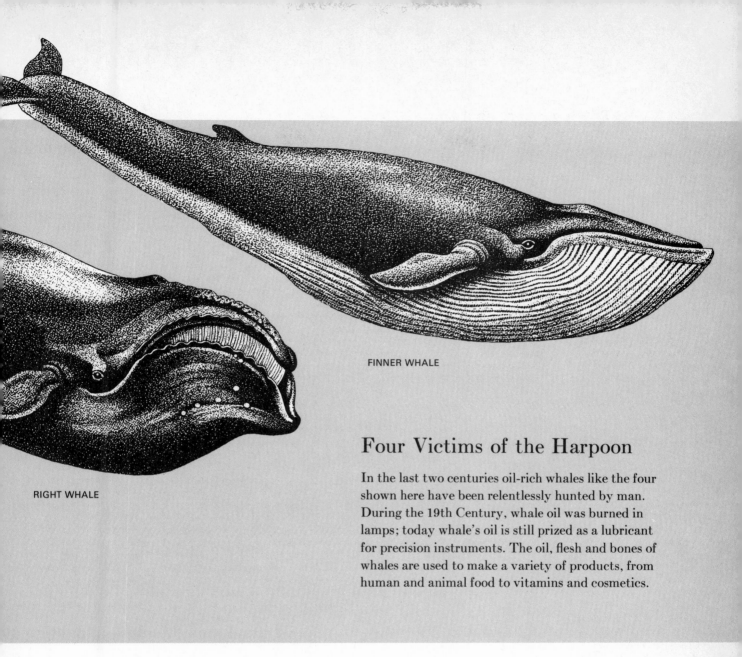

FINNER WHALE

RIGHT WHALE

Four Victims of the Harpoon

In the last two centuries oil-rich whales like the four shown here have been relentlessly hunted by man. During the 19th Century, whale oil was burned in lamps; today whale's oil is still prized as a lubricant for precision instruments. The oil, flesh and bones of whales are used to make a variety of products, from human and animal food to vitamins and cosmetics.

and bear their young at sea, and are very awkward and almost helpless out of water. Female manatees may be responsible for many of the reports of mermaids, those legendary creatures, half fish, half woman. To superstitious sailors viewing manatees at a distance, they resembled mermaids. Up close, however, there can be no confusion, for manatees are homely animals—bald, harelipped, mustached and thick-necked. In fact,

it is a fair assumption that only a male sea cow would find any beauty whatsoever in the female of the species.

What is believed to be the largest surviving group of big meat-eating mammals in the world today consists of about 25 million fin-footed animals of 31 species divided into three groups—the eared seals, the true seals and the walruses. Eared seals, which include sea lions and fur seals, still have visible ears;

A Built-in Food Strainer

Most large whales eat only very tiny ocean animals and plants called plankton. To catch this food, the whales have a feathery strainer called a baleen inside their mouths *(left)*. As a whale swims into a mass of plankton, *(right)* water rushes into its mouth, the plankton snags on the baleen, and the water squirts out the sides of the mouth. When a mouthful of food has built up on the baleen, the whale licks it off with its enormous tongue.

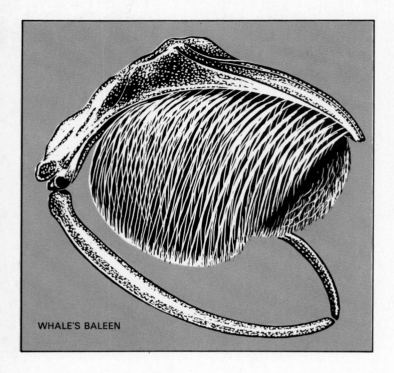

WHALE'S BALEEN

the true seals and walruses have lost these projections, which hamper swift underwater swimming, and in general have moved closer to the streamlined fish shape.

Fur seals were butchered in the north for 200 years. In the Pribilof Islands off Alaska, their numbers were reduced from more than two million to scarcely more than a hundred thousand by the early years of the 20th Century. Since 1911 the United States has administered an international agreement to protect the Pribilof herds. The effect on the seals has been startling; their numbers are now back to about two million.

Sea lions were never hunted with such savagery, largely because they have no great commercial value. One variety is the so-called trained seal, often seen at circuses or in zoos. Even without training, it likes to

toss and catch fish as it frolics off its native Pacific rocks.

True seals range more widely than the eared varieties. One of them, the monk seal, lives in the tropics, a sharp break from the preference of most seals for cold water. The largest true seals are the sea elephants, which grow as big as 16 feet long and 12 feet around and have an odd 15-inch "trunk" hanging down over their noses. Almost exterminated for their blubber, sea elephants are making a comeback in the Antarctic and on Guadalupe Island off Lower California.

A sadder story is that of the walrus. Like its smaller cousin the fur seal, the 3,000-pound walrus was once plentiful throughout the Arctic regions. But hunters pursued it relentlessly because, in addition to its hide and oil, its two-foot tusks commanded a high

price in the ivory market. The cruelest of the hunters' tactics was to catch a walrus calf and beat it until it cried. Since walruses are devoted parents, every adult within hearing would rush to the calf's aid—and into the hunters' trap. Now the few walruses left roam remote areas of Greenland and the Arctic.

Of all the mammals that have taken to the sea, none has made the change more completely than the whale—and none has been more savagely hunted by man. From early times men have been awed by these mighty giants of the deep. Even now, when modern men and their machines have driven most of the big whales to a last antarctic stronghold, it is impossible for most of us to look upon these wonderful animals without being aware of their power and grandeur.

Not all whales are big, of course; some are no more than four-and-a-half feet long. Of the 100-odd species, almost half are the relatively small dolphins and porpoises. There are two basic kinds of whales, into which all species fall: the baleen whales and toothed whales. Baleen whales, which are the biggest of all, have huge strainers of a tough and flexible stuff called whalebone, or baleen, inside their mouths. The whales with teeth include the broad-domed 60-foot-long sperm whale, the killer whale and all the dolphins and porpoises.

The whale is so completely adapted to life in the sea that many people still think of it as a fish. It is easy to see why because, while it is warm-blooded and breathes air, the whale certainly looks like a fish and in many

(Text continued on page 107)

An Ocean Otter

A sea otter, one of the most playful of all ocean mammals, swims along on its back while it eats a shellfish. It opens the mollusk by cracking the shell against a stone that it has placed on its chest (*left*). Mother otters usually hold their babies to protect them, as shown at left below. But sometimes, when mothers go off to hunt for food, they tether their young close to shore with a long piece of seaweed.

ways it lives like a fish. It has no need, as some other sea mammals do, to go on land to bear its young. It is marvelously streamlined. Its neck bones have shortened so that the head merges with the trunk. Its forelegs have become fins and its hind legs have completely disappeared.

The only remains of the whale's external ear are openings on either side of the head no thicker than a pencil. Their nostrils have moved from the front to the very top of the head and have become one or two blowholes that enable the whale to breathe without raising itself more than a few inches above the water's surface. A thick layer of blubber, or fat, not only helps keep it warm in cold polar seas but also acts as a food reserve when the whale travels to warmer waters where the kind of food it likes may not be so abundant.

The biggest whales are bigger than any land animal could be. The largest one ever caught was a female blue whale that measured 113.5 feet and probably weighed 170 tons, as much as 2,267 average men.

A whale can grow to such size because water holds up its weight evenly over its body, thus avoiding the concentrated forces at points of support that land animals must withstand. The whale's great size provides room for the muscles that give the whale swimming power. The entire rear third of a whale is an engine of enormous muscles. These enable the whale's 12-foot tail to move in a semicircular motion that works like a

ship's propeller, building up as much as 520 horsepower in a 90-footer, according to the estimate of one scientist. Large blue whales can travel at 20 knots when necessary, and can run all day ahead of a whaling ship traveling at 10 knots.

All big whales except the sperm whale are baleen whales. They feed on small creatures of the sea by swimming along at slow speed with their mouths open. Their jaws are so wide that a tremendous amount of water pours in and is then forced out at the sides through the baleen strainers, which hang down like a curtain. Great numbers of tiny marine animals are caught in the baleen as the water passes through. Every now and then the whale's tongue wipes the baleen clean and passes the food back to its gullet.

Many whales pass about six months of the year in polar waters, where the feeding is best, and then travel to tropical seas to breed and bear young, undoubtedly so that their babies will have warm water to swim in until they grow a protective coat of blubber under their skins.

The female blue whale generally gives birth to a single calf every other year. Female blues are somewhat bigger than their mates, and their calves are astonishingly large—23 feet at birth in the case of a typical blue-whale calf, or almost a third the size of its mother. For seven months the female blue nurses its baby, supplying the calf with a ton of very rich milk a day, according to one estimate, while lying still on the surface of the sea. By the time the blue calf is ready to seek out food for itself, it is more than 50 feet long, as long as full-grown whales of many species. By the time it is two years old it may be 75 feet long.

The sperm whale, whose oil provided the wealth of New England's great 19th Century whaling industry, is in many respects the most interesting of all whales. It is the only big whale with teeth, which are like pegs about eight inches long. The teeth are all in the lower jaw, and they fit into holes in the leathery upper jaw when the long narrow mouth is snapped shut. The sperm whale needs its teeth to fight and kill its favorite food, the giant squid. It dives down more than half a mile to feed, nosing along the bottom for squid and octopus, sometimes staying there for 40 minutes before coming up to blow. Blowing, or spouting, is simply the exhalation of a whale, a great mixture of stale air and water vapor ejected into the air.

The sperm whale's name is derived from spermaceti, the oily wax found in a storage tank located in its huge square-fronted head. Spermaceti is lighter than water, and scientists formerly believed that this material helped the animal to stay afloat. Now it is thought to be connected with the whale's amazing ability to dive deep and come up relatively speedily without suffering the "bends," the agonizing pains that humans

get when they surface too rapidly from a dive.

Whales cannot breathe while underwater, naturally. But their enormous lungs help them stay submerged for astonishingly long periods of time—60 to 90 minutes. If they stay underwater too long, of course, they drown like other mammals. This fact has provided proof that sperm whales do dive deep. Every once in a while a drowned whale is found entangled in a transoceanic cable. A cable-repair ship once found a dead whale caught in a cable at a depth of 3,720 feet.

The sperm whale's appetite for giant squid is the source of one of the ocean's most valuable products. The whale swallows squid whole, but has never been able to digest the hard parrotlike beaks of its prey. These some-

The Gentle Dugong

Sea-dwelling mammals, like the dugongs, have specialized forms that have evolved as they adapted to life in the water. The dugong, for instance, has flippers instead of forelegs. Its outer ears have disappeared to give it a more streamlined shape, and even its heavy bones help it stay under water.

The Streamlined Dolphin

The white-sided dolphin shown here has a body shape so well suited to life in the water that in many ways it looks like a fish. Dolphins communicate with each other by a wide variety of calls and noises. They are very friendly and playful animals that often frolic around the bow of a passing ship.

Special Skeletons for the Sea

The skeletons of a porpoise *(below)* and of a sea lion *(below, right)* show some similarities to the bones of land mammals, but also some changes suited to life in the water. Most mammals, for instance, have five "finger" bones. These are present in the sea lion's front limbs, but only four remain in the porpoise. Like land mammals, the sea lion still has its hind legs. But the porpoise has lost them entirely. Instead, the porpoise has an extra-thick backbone that gives it added swimming strength.

times fail to pass through the digestive tract, causing the gradual formation of a dark, sticky material called ambergris. It smells foul at first, but after processing becomes the best substance known for making perfumes hold their scent. In recent years substitute products have tended to take the place of ambergris in perfumes, but top-grade ambergris is still worth as much as $10 per ounce. Whales frequently succeed in vomiting up their ambergris, in which case it may be found floating in the water or washed up on a beach. It is also found when a whale is captured and cut up.

No one has yet figured out an intelligence test for whales. But smaller sea mammals, the dolphins, have been studied in captivity,

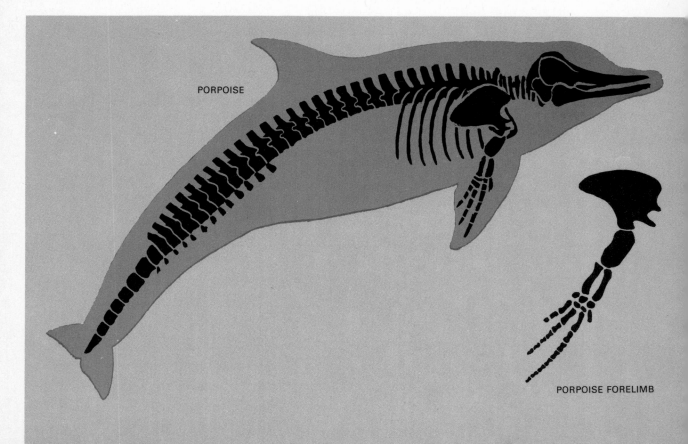

PORPOISE

PORPOISE FORELIMB

and have shown considerable ability to learn. Dolphins are social animals, with a tender regard for their young and a readiness to go to the aid of a fellow dolphin in distress. When a dolphin is injured, for example, other dolphins gather around and try to push the wounded member of their school up to the surface so that it can breathe.

Dolphins make high, sharp chirps and squeaks to talk to each other. These chirps also help them find food, for they have an organ that works like sonar, the underwater detection device; using their own "sonar," dolphins can trace the echoes that bounce off food and locate their meals.

Whales, like dolphins, live in social groups and seem to have ways of using sound to communicate with each other and to locate masses of tiny marine organisms. But the whale has not been able to cope with its one great enemy, man. In the past two and a half centuries, man has hunted and slaughtered one species of whale after another.

The first species brought near to extinction was the Atlantic right whale. Whalers of the 17th Century called this black, oil-rich 60-footer a "right" whale because it floated when killed; most other whales were "wrong" because they sank when killed and so were lost. The Atlantic right whale was almost gone by the end of the 17th Century, whereupon whalers next gave chase to the bowhead, also known as the Greenland or Arctic

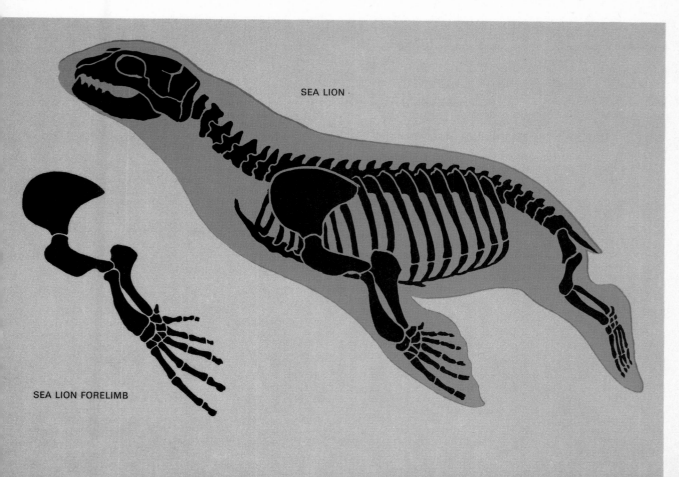

SEA LION

SEA LION FORELIMB

right whale, whose mouthful of baleen alone could bring $10,000 in world markets. For in those days all fashionable women wore corsets make out of whalebone. Bowheads, in consequence, were soon all but wiped out.

In the last year of the United States Civil War a Norwegian whaling man invented a gun for firing grenade-carrying harpoons, and shortly afterward other Norwegians developed power-driven catcher boats and devices for pumping air into captured whales to keep them from sinking. These refinements revolutionized the whaling industry, making it possible for whalers to go after the big whales —the blue, the fin, the humpback—that had been "wrong" for earlier mariners. Today the big whales have almost vanished from the Northern Hemisphere. In the Antarctic, whalers operating giant whaling-factory ships have killed over one million whales in the past 50 years. Though international agreements have limited the annual catch since 1932, it has been estimated that the efficient slaughterers of the 20th Century have killed five times as many whales as all the famous whaling fleets of the 19th Century put to-

gether. At present, some experts believe that there are fewer than 50,000 fin whales left in the Antarctic. How much longer they can survive depends on what restrictions are placed on hunting them. During one recent season alone, whalers killed 27,128. For the magnificent blue whale, the point of no return may already have passed. In spite of the fact that the hunting of blue whales has been sharply restricted since 1946, the number seen and caught continues to decline. It may be that blue whales are now so few that they are unable to find mates. Unlike the smaller gray whale, which has been saved from extinction by the fact that the surviving few always return to two or three Lower California bays to breed, the blue whale has no such regular habits. Its breeding depends on chance encounters in the open sea as the huge beasts range from Antarctica all the way north to the equator. How, in all these vast ocean reaches, are the surviving blue whales to meet others of their kind? Even though all hunting of the blue whale has been banned, the next decades may well see the disappearance of the most gigantic creature ever to live on earth.

Highly Intelligent Mammals

Four dolphins seem to grin as they wait for a handout of fish at Marineland in California. Dolphins have complicated brains comparable to man's, making them responsive to training They delight visitors with a variety of stunts like jumping through hoops and playing games of basketball.

8
Man and the Future of the Sea

The seas are mankind's last frontier on this planet. For ages man has treated the great waters as little more than hunting grounds for fishermen and highways for ships. Now he is awakening to see that beneath the waves lies a vast, unexplored territory every bit as challenging as outer space and much more promising in terms of reward. Man, at last, is gaining the scientific know-how to meet the challenge of the sea, and his growing needs for food, water, minerals and power give him strong reasons for doing so.

During the last few years, scientists have been taking giant steps toward learning about the land under the oceans. Despite the great difficulty of working in the depths, an encouraging beginning has been made in mapping the sea bottom. Exploration under water is more dangerous than trips into space

ASTRIDE SCAFFOLDING, a Southeast Asian fisherman adjusts his nets. The seas have long been a means of food and travel, but man has only recently begun to use this part of his planet more effectively. New ways are being found to extract food, mine undersea minerals, and quickly cross the vast oceans.

because the pressure on the underwater explorer from the weight of the water above him is immense. At a depth of 1,000 feet, there is more than 450 pounds of pressure per square inch on man's body. This is more than 30 times as much as the pressure felt in the open air.

If the deep-sea diver rises too fast to the surface, the rapid decrease of pressure on his body may cause bubbles of gas to form in his tissues and blood. These bubbles bring on decompression sickness, or "the bends," a painful disease that may cripple or kill.

In the past, these dangers made detailed exploration of the land under the sea difficult, if not impossible. The thought of man living in the sea itself was dismissed as a fantasy. Yet recent tests have proved that man can survive and work at depths of several hundred feet. This newly discovered ability to live under water stems from the recent development of new ways to protect divers from the pressures of the deep.

The old-fashioned diving suit was made of heavy, waterproof material attached to a metal helmet. The divers received air through rubber hoses—the "life lines"—that extended to ships on the surface. In these suits, a man could descend into the water, but he could not stay down long, and he spent most of his day in a very slow ascent to avoid the

Harvesting the Ocean Crops

Fishing with methods ranging from primitive to sophisticated, man annually catches some 40 million tons of fish. Australian aborigines fish much as their ancestors did, with spears from canoes (*above*). In contrast, an American fleet off the Carolinas (*left*) uses electronic gear to locate schools of fish. Man's next step in harvesting the seas may be aquaculture —the controlled planting and raising of fish.

117

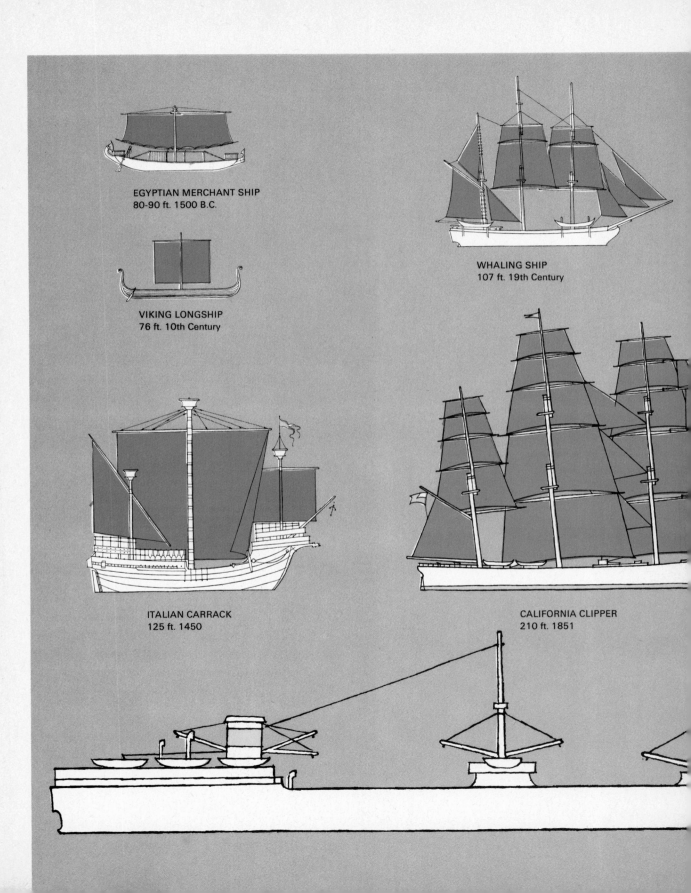

EGYPTIAN MERCHANT SHIP
80-90 ft. 1500 B.C.

VIKING LONGSHIP
76 ft. 10th Century

WHALING SHIP
107 ft. 19th Century

ITALIAN CARRACK
125 ft. 1450

CALIFORNIA CLIPPER
210 ft. 1851

Progress on the Seas

In his long struggle to master the sea, man has launched an enormous variety of ships. His first major advance after the crude prehistoric dugout was craft propelled by oars or a sail, such as the Egyptian merchant ship and the Viking longship (*far left*). Pushed by a need to explore and aided by improved technology, man began building larger ships with many sails. This age was typified by far-ranging vessels like the Italian carrack and the whaling and clipper ships of the 19th Century. The present-day era of steam power began after 1807, the year Robert Fulton built the steam-driven *Clermont*. Now, long steel ships like the whale factory—over two football fields long—are not unusual.

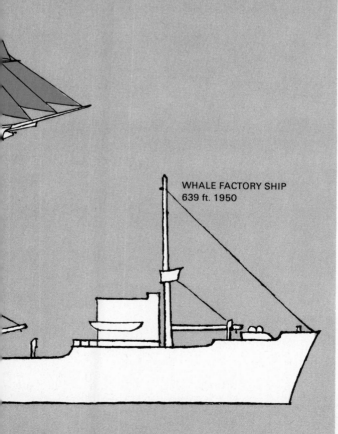

WHALE FACTORY SHIP
639 ft. 1950

effects of a sudden decrease of pressure. The invention of the aqualung—air fed directly to the diver's mouth from tanks of oxygen strapped onto his back—gave man greater mobility under water, but did not eliminate the problem of pressure.

Then in the late 1950s, a U.S. Navy captain, George F. Bond, came up with a startling new way to live under water. His method is called "saturation diving." Divers enter a chamber that is pressurized and filled to capacity with a mixture of helium and oxygen. After about 24 hours, the tissues in the diver's body are fully saturated by the gases. Then when the chamber is lowered under water, the diver can live and sleep inside for weeks at a time without bothering about decompression.

Because the chamber is pressurized from the beginning, the diver can move in and out to explore under the sea whenever he wishes. This is not possible with a conventional underwater vessel, like a submarine, whose interior is kept at the same pressure as the surface air above. Therefore, if there was a direct opening into the water, the heavier pressure of the water would force it into the submarine. In the undersea capsules, on the other hand, the pressure inside is the same as the water pressure outside. Thus, when special hatches are opened, no water will enter. The divers can move in and out of the capsule freely. And when the capsule is brought back to the surface, the divers can stay inside as long as necessary during decompression, thus preventing a dreaded attack of "the bends."

Bond's idea has worked excellently in practice. Several experiments in undersea living in pressurized chambers have been remarkably successful. The famed French underwater explorer Captain Jacques-Yves Cousteau and a crew of seven men spent a month in a special capsule five fathoms under the Red Sea in 1963. One of the most dramatic experiments took place in 1965, when the U.S. Navy lowered a shelter called *Sealab II* into the cold waters off La Jolla, California. Three teams of 10 men each took turns living in *Sealab II* more than 200 feet below the surface. The men moved in and out of the capsule, testing their ability to do manual labor, explore and conduct experiments. One man, the former astronaut Scott Carpenter, stayed down with *Sealab II* for 30 consecutive days. Beginning in 1969, Project Tektite did *Sealab II* one better: four aquanauts spent 60 days some 40 feet below the surface at Great Lameshur Bay in the Virgin Islands. Moving in and out of their habitat, they studied marine life and were themselves studied to see how well they adjusted to undersea living.

Projects like *Sealab II* and Tektite show that man can live and work under water for long periods. But all the experiments have been done in shallow waters above the continental shelf. The very deep waters beyond the shelf where ocean valleys plunge thousands of feet make up most of the

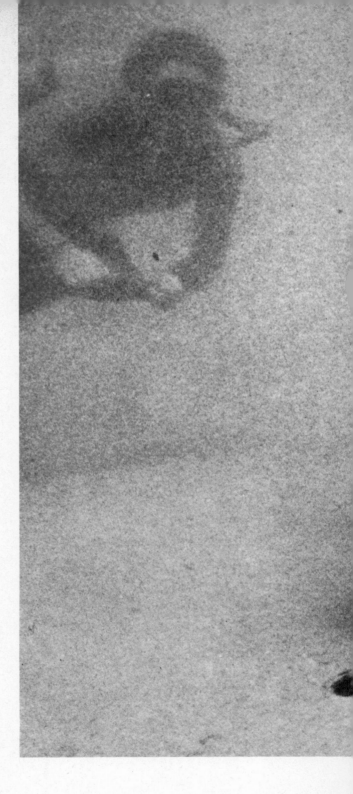

A New Underwater Freedom

A skin diver probes for evidence of underwater oil deposits.
He wears a portable air supply on his back. Once, man could
stay beneath the water only as long as his breath held out;
now, equipment such as this has given him a new mobility.

121

Traveling into the Deep

The three craft below are answers to a serious problem faced by underwater explorers: the pressure of deep water. On land, an average force of 15 pounds presses on every square inch of a man's body. Under water, the forces increase tremendously; at 6,000 feet, the pressure is 2,780 pounds per square inch. The problem is to build craft sturdy enough to withstand the pressure, but maneuverable enough to perform useful work. The *Alvin*, designed to work at 6,000 feet, has air-filled spheres near the rear for buoyancy and a mechanical arm in front for probing. The *Archimedes* can descend seven miles; metal pellets help it sink, and when released enable it to rise. The *Aluminaut* has a strong aluminum hull; it can dive to 15,000 feet, where 62 per cent of the ocean floor is within range.

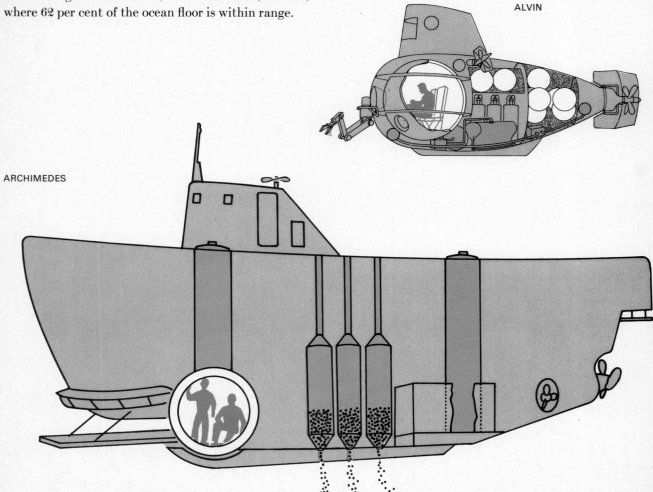

ALVIN

ARCHIMEDES

oceans, and they provide an even sterner test for divers and undersea vehicles.

Now, diving craft are being designed that will be able to descend to the bottom of the deepest known part of the ocean—the 36,-000-foot Marianas Trench off Guam. These huge diving craft will be bubbles made of 2¾-inch-thick glass. Since glass grows stronger under pressure, these spheres should be able to withstand about 30,000 pounds per square inch—twice that of the water in the bottom of the Marianas Trench.

Another project is the development of five deep-submergence rescue vehicles (DSRV is the Navy abbreviation). In the event of a submarine disaster, the DSRV will be carried to the scene of the accident by conventional submarines, and then launched as deep as 6,000 feet. Other subs being planned

will be able to go down to 20,000 feet; such boats will open up almost all of the ocean's floor to exploration.

For economic reasons alone, man can no longer afford to ignore the seas. The fact is that the lands below the oceans hold treasures that would be the envy of the richest countries on earth. It has been estimated that the sea contains about 50 million million metric tons of minerals. These include magnesium, uranium, manganese (the U.S. must import almost 2 million tons of this mineral a year, for steel and battery production) as well as the classic riches of gold and silver. And there is enough copper and aluminum in the 40 million square miles of ocean bottom to supply man for a million years at the present rate of use.

Much of this valuable raw material is still untouched. But one vital mineral—oil—is

ALUMINAUT

being drawn in increasingly large amounts from beneath relatively shallow parts of the sea. More than 16 per cent of all the oil drilled in the world comes from offshore wells. Experts predict that by 1975 the total will be close to 40 per cent. So many oil-drilling platforms have already been erected in the Gulf of Mexico that they are interfering with the normal shipping lanes.

Fresh water is another unsuspected resource to be gained from the salty seas. Even now many ocean vessels desalt sea water for use on the ship. But the process of filtering out the salt so that the water can be used on land has always been too expensive. However, recent experiments with improved machinery are bringing the costs down. New York has even started building a plant on Long Island that will draw the salt from sea water and make it fresh. An even more remarkable way of securing fresh water will be to tap the springs in the ocean floor and pipe the sweet water back to the land.

Of all the sea's possibilities, the greatest is its promise for increasing the world's food supply. Scientists believe that, mile for mile, the sea can someday produce more food than the land. Yet at present the oceans supply only 2 per cent of man's food. This is because man generally does not sow and harvest the sea; he hunts with no thought of tomorrow. In some areas, of course, men do "farm" the seas; they lay out oyster or fish beds, fence them in against predators and use scientific methods of breeding to increase the yield. To meet the vast future needs of of an ever-increasing world population, man will have to start farming the seas as thoroughly as he farms the land.

These are a few of the treasures locked away in the ocean. Man has begun his assault on the sea, and he is certain to continue the effort. But sometime in the future the sea itself must come to an end. Astronomers predict that the sun will pass through a "red giant" stage before turning into a cold, dark lump of matter drifting through space. This will not happen for at least three billion years—perhaps not for 10 billion years. But when the sun does turn into a red giant, it will swell up to nearly 100 times its present size, emitting immense quantities of heat in the process. In its red light the earth's temperature will rise, causing life to shrivel, and then the seas will finally boil away in clouds of steam.

A Taste of Tomorrow Today

When the U.S. Navy submarine 571—the *Nautilus*—first slid into the water in 1955, it signaled the start of a new era in man's relation to the sea. The *Nautilus* was the world's first atomic-powered vessel. Nuclear energy has increased the range and speed of specially designed ships—and has made the seas seem smaller.

Index

Numerals in italics indicate a photograph or painting of the subject listed.

Credits

The sources for the illustrations that appear in this book are shown below. Credits for the pictures from left to right are separated by commas, from top to bottom by dashes.

Cover—John Severson
Table of Contents—Leslie Martin—Jim Egleson—Otto van Eersel—Matt Greene—Leslie Martin—Kenneth Gosner of the Newark Museum—Rudolf Freund—James Alexander
6, 7—Fritz Goro
8, 9—Ward's Natural Science Establishment, Leslie Martin
10, 11—Andreas Feininger, Rudolf Freund
13—Matt Greene (2), Nino Carbé
14, 15—Anthony Petrocelli
16, 17—Leslie Martin, René Martin
18, 19—Rudolf Freund
20, 21—Rudolf Freund
23—Official U.S. Navy Photo
24—Conrad Limbaugh
26, 27—Jim Egleson
29 to 37—Kenneth Fagg

39—Jim Egleson
41—Courtesy Dr. N. L. Kenkevitch
42, 43—Werner Wolff
44 to 48—Otto van Eersel
51—Dr. Robert C. Murphy
52—Edward Rowe Snow
54 to 56—Matt Greene
58, 59—Michael Rougier
60—drawing by Jack J. Kunz, Dr. Douglas P. Wilson (2)—M. A. Wilson
63—Eliot Elisofon
64, 65—Kenneth Gosner of the Newark Museum
67—Otto van Eersel—Ben Goode
68, 69—Otto van Eersel—Leslie Martin (3)
70, 71—Otto van Eersel—Leslie Martin

72, 73—Otto van Eersel, Leslie Martin (4)
74, 75—Otto van Eersel, Ben Goode (3)
76, 77—Otto van Eersel, Ben Goode (2)
78, 79—Jack J. Kunz (2), Otto van Eersel
80—Otto van Eersel, Leslie Martin
81—Leslie Martin, Otto van Eersel
82, 83—Otto van Eersel, Leslie Martin (2), Matt Greene—Leslie Martin
84, 85—Otto van Eersel, Fritz Goro
86—Russ Kinne
88, 89—Peter Stackpole
90, 91—Kenneth Gosner of the Newark Museum
93—Kenneth Gosner of the

Newark Museum
95—Kenneth Gosner of the Newark Museum
96—Peter Stackpole
98, 99—Rudolf Freund, Virginia Wells
100, 101—Rudolf Freund
102, 103—Kenneth Gosner of the Newark Museum
104, 105—Fritz Goro
106—Jack Schoenharr
108, 109—Guy Tudor
110, 111—Kenneth Gosner of the Newark Museum
113—Peter Stackpole
114, 115—Michael Rougier
116, 117—Hank Walker, upper right Fritz Goro
118, 119—James Alexander
122, 123—Matt Greene
125—Ralph Morse
End papers—Virginia Wells

For Further Reading

Abbot, R. Tucker. *Sea Shells of the World*. Golden Press, 1962.

Annov, Boris Jr. and H.M.S. Mindlin, *Wonders of the Deep Sea*. Hale, 1965.

Arnold, Oren, *Marvels of the Sea and Shore*. Abelard, 1963.

Brindze, Ruth, *All About Undersea Exploration*. Random House, 1960.

Buck, Margaret Waring, *Along the Seashore*. Abingdon, 1964.

Carson, Rachel L., *The Sea Around Us*. Oxford Univ. Press, 1961.

Clarke, Arthur C., *The Challenge of the Sea*. Holt, 1960.

Coggins, Jack, *Hydrospace: Frontier Beneath the Sea*. Dodd, 1966.

Dugan, James, *Undersea Explorer: The Story of Captain Cousteau*. Harper, 1957.

Epstein, Sam and Beryl, *First Book of the Ocean*. Watts, 1961.

Fairbridge, Rhodes W., *The Encyclopedia of Oceanography*. Reinhold, 1966.

Fenton, Carroll L. and Mildred A., *In Prehistoric Seas*. Doubleday, 1963.

Goldin, Augusta, *The Bottom of the Sea*. Crowell, 1966.

Hawes, Judy, *Shrimps*. Crowell, 1966.

Hess, Lilo, *Sea Horses*. Scribners, 1966.

Jacobs, Lou Jr., *Wonders of an Oceanarium*. Golden Gate, 1965.

Kavaler, Lucy, *The Wonders of Algae*. Day, 1961.

Kinney, Jean, *What Does the Tide Do?* Young Scott Books, 1966.

Lauber, Patricia, *The Friendly Dolphins*. Random House, 1963.

National Geographic Society, *Man, Ships and the Sea*. National Geographic Society, 1962.

Reidman, Sarah R. and Elton T. Gustafson, *Home is the Sea: For Whales*. Rand McNally, 1966.

Selsam, Millicent E., *See Along the Shore*. Harper, 1961.

Selsam, Millicent E., *Underwater Zoos*. Morrow, 1961.

Shannon, Terry and Charles Payzant, *Project Sealab: The Story of the United States Navy's Man-in-the-Sea Program*. Golden Gate, 1966.

Vogel, Helen W. and Mary L. Caruso, *Ocean Harvest*. Knopf, 1961.

Zim, Herbert S., *Sharks*. Morrow, 1966.

Acknowledgments

The editors are indebted to Ross Nigrelli, Director, New York Aquarium, Brooklyn, N.Y. and Xavier Le Pichon, Research Associate, Oceanography Department, Lamont Observatory, Columbia University, N.Y., who read the text and commented on their respective areas of study. The editors are also indebted to the staff of the LIFE Nature Library edition of *The Sea*, from which this volume has been adapted. The staff for this edition was Stanley Fillmore, editor; Eric Gluckman, designer; Peter Chaitin, Tony Chiu, John von Hartz, writers; Eleanor Feltser, Susan Marcus, Theo Pascal, researchers; Eleanore W. Karsten, copyreader; Virginia Wells, art assistant.